SQA

2019 SQA Specimen and Past Papers with Answers

Higher
CHEMISTRY

D1477176

2018 & 2019 Exams
and 2018 Specimen Question Paper

**HODDER
GIBSON**
AN HACHETTE UK COMPAN

This book contains the official SQA 2018 and 2019 Exams, and the 2018 Specimen Question Paper for Higher Chemistry, with associated SQA-approved answers modified from the official marking instructions that accompany the paper.

In addition the book contains study skills advice. This advice has been specially commissioned by Hodder Gibson, and has been written by experienced senior teachers and examiners in line with the Higher syllabus and assessment outlines. This is not SQA material but has been devised to provide further guidance for Higher examinations.

Every effort has been made to trace the copyright holders and to obtain their permission for the use of copyright material. Hodder Gibson will be happy to receive information allowing us to rectify any error or omission in future editions.

Hachette UK's policy is to use papers that are natural, renewable and recyclable products and made from wood grown in well-managed forests and other controlled sources. The logging and manufacturing processes are expected to conform to the environmental regulations of the country of origin.

Orders: please contact Bookpoint Ltd, 130 Park Drive, Milton Park, Abingdon, Oxon OX14 4SE. Telephone: (44) 01235 827827. Fax: (44) 01235 400454. Lines are open 9.00–5.00, Monday to Friday, with a 24-hour message answering service. Visit our website at www.hoddereducation.co.uk. If you have queries or questions that aren't about an order, you can contact us at: hoddergibson@hodder.co.uk

This collection first published in 2019 by
Hodder Gibson, an imprint of Hodder Education,
An Hachette UK Company
211 St Vincent Street
Glasgow G2 5QY

Typeset by Aptara, Inc.

Printed in the UK

A catalogue record for this title is available from the British Library

ISBN: 978-1-5104-7824-4

2 1

2020 2019

MIX
Paper from
responsible sources
FSC™ C104740

SCOTLAND EXCEL

We are an approved supplier on the Scotland Excel framework.

Schools can find us on their procurement system as:

Hodder & Stoughton Limited
t/a Hodder Gibson.

Introduction

Higher Chemistry

The Course

The main aims of the Higher Chemistry course are for learners to:

- develop and apply knowledge and understanding of chemistry
- develop an understanding of chemistry's role in scientific issues and relevant applications of chemistry, including the impact these could make in society and the environment
- develop scientific analytical thinking skills, including scientific evaluation, in a chemistry context
- develop the use of technology, equipment and materials, safely, in practical scientific activities, including using risk assessments
- develop scientific inquiry, investigative, problem solving and planning skills
- use and understand scientific literacy to communicate ideas and issues and to make scientifically informed choices
- develop skills of independent working.

How the Course is assessed

There are two parts to the Higher Chemistry assessment:

1. An assignment worth 20% of your overall course mark
2. A multiple choice exam and an extended-response exam, worth 80% of your overall course mark

You will carry out your assignment during class time and write a report, summarising your findings, under exam conditions. Your report will be marked by the SQA and contributes 20% to the overall course mark.

The course award is graded A–D, the grade being determined by the total mark you score in the examination and the mark you gain in the assignment.

The Examination

The written exam comprises two question papers: a multiple choice exam worth 25 marks, and an extended-response paper, worth 95 marks. You will be given 40 minutes to answer the multiple choice questions and 2 hours 20 minutes to answer the extended-response questions. Overall, the written exams contribute 80% to the overall course mark.

Key Tips For Your Success

Practise! Practise! Practise!

In common with Higher Mathematics and the other Higher sciences, the key to exam success in Chemistry is to prepare by regularly answering questions. Use the questions as a prompt for further study: if you find that you cannot answer a question, review your notes and/or textbook to help you find the necessary knowledge to answer the question. You will quickly find out what you can/cannot do if you invest time attempting to answer questions. It is a much more valuable use of time than passively copying notes, which is a common trap many students fall into!

The data booklet

The data booklet contains formulae and useful data, which you will have to use in the exam. Although you might think that you have a good memory for chemical data (such as the symbols for elements or the atomic mass of an element) always check using the data booklet.

Calculations

In preparation for the exam, ensure that you recognise the different calculation types:

- relative rate
- using bond enthalpy
- using $cm\Delta T$
- percentage yield
- atom economy
- using molar volume
- volumetric calculations
- calculations from balanced chemical equations

You will encounter these calculations in the exam so it's worth spending time practising to ensure that you are familiar with the routines for solving these problems. Even if you are not sure how to attempt a calculation question, show your working! You will be given credit for calculations, which are relevant to the problem being solved.

Explain questions

You will encounter questions, which ask you to *explain your answer*. Take your time and attempt to explain to the examiner. If you can use a diagram or chemical equations to aid your answer, use these as they can really bring an answer to life.

Applying your knowledge of practical chemistry

As part of your Higher Chemistry experience, you should have had plenty of practice carrying out experiments using standard lab equipment and you should have had opportunities to evaluate your results from experiments. In the Higher exam, you are expected to be familiar with the techniques and apparatus listed in the tables below.

Apparatus

Beaker	Dropper	Pipette filler
Boiling tube/ Test tubes	Evaporating basin	Distillation flask
Burette	Funnel	Thermometer
Conical flask	Measuring cylinder	Volumetric flask
Delivery tubes	Pipette	Condenser

Techniques

Distillation
Filtration
Methods for collecting a gas: over water or using a gas syringe
Safe heating methods: using a Bunsen, water bath or heating mantle
Titration
Use of a balance, including measuring mass by difference
Determining enthalpy changes

The following general points about experimental chemistry are worth noting:

- A pipette is more accurate than a measuring cylinder for measuring fixed volumes of liquid. A burette can be used to measure non-standard volumes of liquid.
- A standard flask is used to make up a standard solution i.e. a solution of accurately known concentration. This is done by dissolving a known mass of solute in water and transferring to the standard flask with rinsings. Finally, the standard flask is made up to the mark with water.
- A gas syringe is an excellent method for measuring the volume of gas produced from an experiment.
- Bunsen burners cannot be used near flammable substances.
- A Bunsen burner does not allow you to control the rate of heating.

Analysis of data

From your experience working with experimental data you should know how to calculate averages, how to eliminate rogue data, how to draw graphs (scatter and best fit line/curve) and how to interpret graphs.

It is common in Higher exams to be presented with titration data such as the data shown in the table below.

Titration	Volume, cm^3
1	28.0
2	21.1
3	21.0
4	21.2
5	34.0

You should be able to look at a table of titration results like this and conclude:

    (a) Titration 1 is a rough result.

    (b) Titrations 2, 3 and 4 are concordant, i.e. they are within $0.2\,cm^3$ of each other.

    (c) The average titre is the sum of all concordant results divided by the number of concordant results. In this case, average titre =
$$\frac{21.1 + 21.0 + 21.2}{3} = 21.1\,cm^3$$

    (d) Titration 5 is a rogue result or outlier, probably caused by experimental error.

Numeracy

The Higher Chemistry exam will contain several questions that test your numeracy skills e.g. calculating relative rate, enthalpy changes, percentage yield etc. Other questions will ask you to "scale up" or "scale down" as this is a skill that is used by practising scientists in their day to day job.

Being able to deal with proportion is key to answering numeracy questions in chemistry. A common layout is shown in the examples below. In all cases, the unknown (what you are being asked to calculate) should be put on the right hand side.

[Example]

The enthalpy of combustion of ethanol is $-1367\,kJ\,mol^{-1}$.

Calculate the theoretical amount of energy that could be released by burning 10 g of ethanol.

Solution

This question is about proportion. A good way to tackle such a question is to establish a relationship between two quantities and then scale to 1. Here, the relationship is between mass (since we are asked about 10 g) and energy.

Whatever you are asked to calculate (in this case energy) put it on the right-hand side, i.e.

Mass ➡ Energy

Since you are told that the energy is $-1367\,kJ\,mol^{-1}$, you should be able to calculate the mass of ethanol since the energy is for 1 mol = GFM. For ethanol, 1 mol = 46 g.

Step 1: Establish a relationship

46 g ➡ −1367 kJ

Step 2: Scale to 1

1 g ➡ $\dfrac{-1367}{46} = -29.717\,kJ$

Step 3: Calculate for the quantity you are asked.

10 g ➡ $10 \times -29.72 = \mathbf{-297.17\,kJ}$

[Example]

A 100 ml bottle of children's paracetamol costs £3.85. The ingredients label states that each 5 ml dose contains 120 mg of paracetamol. Calculate the cost per mg of paracetamol.

Answer:

Volume		Mass
5 ml	➡	120 mg
1 ml	➡	24 mg
100 ml	➡	2400 mg

i.e. 1 bottle contains 2400 mg of paracetamol

Mass		Cost
2400 mg	➡	£3.85
1 mg	➡	£0.0016

Open-ended questions

Real-life chemistry problems rarely have a fixed answer. In the Higher exam, you will encounter two 3 mark questions that are open-ended, i.e. there is more than one "correct" answer. You will recognise these questions from the phrase *using your knowledge of chemistry* in the question. To tackle these, look at the following example.

[Example]

Carbon compounds contribute to our everyday lives as chemists have discovered their usefulness in making foods and cosmetics. Using your knowledge of chemistry, comment on the type of carbon compounds that are likely to be found in food and cosmetics.

Your answer should include typical structures and explain some properties of the compounds which relate to their use.

Author's suggested answer

The beauty of an open-ended question like this is that there are so many carbon compounds you could discuss. The key to answering this question is to think about the carbon compounds you encountered in National 5. Then, think about some of the reactions or properties which would make them useful for the areas mentioned.

As the question states, you should detail your answer with typical structures so that you can show the examiner that you know your chemistry!

The table below lists *some* compounds you could discuss with some details of properties you could mention.

Compound	Comments on properties	Typical structure
Esters	Often have fruity tastes so used as flavourings. Often have pleasant smells so can be used in perfumes etc. You could discuss the fact that esters are non-polar so can dissolve non-polar compounds, e.g. used as the solvent in nail varnish.	
Aldehydes and Ketones	Flavour molecules found in foods. Used as solvents for cosmetics.	
Carboxylic acids	Ethanoic acid is the acid found in vinegar. Has a specific taste.	
Antioxidants	Antioxidants, such as vitamins C and E, are added to food and cosmetics to prevent the food/cosmetic oxidising.	
Soaps	Long chain hydrocarbons (hydrophobic) with a carboxylate head (hydrophilic) which can remove greasy stains.	*hydrophobic group* *hydrophilic group* a soap

You would not be expected to cover all these compounds. A good answer could cover just two examples but would give lots of details on the compounds' properties and structures.

You could also discuss alcohols, detergents, emulsifiers, terpenes, etc.

Good luck!

If you have followed the advice given in this introduction you will be well prepared for the Higher exam. When you sit the exam, take your time and use the experience as an opportunity to show the examiner how much you know. And good luck!

Study Skills – what you need to know to pass exams!

General exam revision: 20 top tips

When preparing for exams, it is easy to feel unsure of where to start or how to revise. This guide to general exam revision provides a good starting place, and, as these are very general tips, they can be applied to all your exams.

1. Start revising in good time.

Don't leave revision until the last minute – this will make you panic and it will be difficult to learn. Make a revision timetable that counts down the weeks to go.

2. Work to a study plan.

Set up sessions of work spread through the weeks ahead. Make sure each session has a focus and a clear purpose. What will you study, when and why? Be realistic about what you can achieve in each session, and don't be afraid to adjust your plans as needed.

3. Make sure you know exactly when your exams are.

Get your exam dates from the SQA website and use the timetable builder tool to create your own exam schedule. You will also get a personalised timetable from your school, but this might not be until close to the exam period.

4. Make sure that you know the topics that make up each course.

Studying is easier if material is in manageable chunks – why not use the SQA topic headings or create your own from your class notes? Ask your teacher for help on this if you are not sure.

5. Break the chunks up into even smaller bits.

The small chunks should be easier to cope with. Remember that they fit together to make larger ideas. Even the process of chunking down will help!

6. Ask yourself these key questions for each course:

- Are all topics compulsory or are there choices?
- Which topics seem to come up time and time again?
- Which topics are your strongest and which are your weakest?

Use your answers to these questions to work out how much time you will need to spend revising each topic.

7. Make sure you know what to expect in the exam.

The subject-specific introduction to this book will help with this. Make sure you can answer these questions:

- How is the paper structured?
- How much time is there for each part of the exam?
- What types of question are involved? These will vary depending on the subject so read the subject-specific section carefully.

8. Past papers are a vital *revision tool!*

Use past papers to support your revision wherever possible. This book contains the answers and mark schemes too – refer to these carefully when checking your work. Using the mark scheme is useful; even if you don't manage to get all the marks available first time when you first practise, it helps you identify how to extend and develop your answers to get more marks next time – and of course, in the real exam.

9. Use study methods that work well for you.

People study and learn in different ways. Reading and looking at diagrams suits some students. Others prefer to listen and hear material – what about reading out loud or getting a friend or family member to do this for you? You could also record and play back material.

10. There are three tried and tested ways to make material stick in your long-term memory:

- Practising – e.g. rehearsal, repeating
- Organising – e.g. making drawings, lists, diagrams, tables, memory aids
- Elaborating – e.g. incorporating the material into a story or an imagined journey

11. Learn actively.

Most people prefer to learn actively – for example, making notes, highlighting, redrawing and redrafting, making up memory aids, or writing past paper answers. A good way to stay engaged and inspired is to mix and match these methods – find the combination that best suits you. This is likely to vary depending on the topic or subject.

12. Be an expert.

Be sure to have a few areas in which you feel you are an expert. This often works because at least some of them will come up, which can boost confidence.

13. Try some visual methods.

Use symbols, diagrams, charts, flashcards, post-it notes etc. Don't forget – the brain takes in chunked images more easily than loads of text.

14. Remember – practice makes perfect.

Work on difficult areas again and again. Look and read – then test yourself. You cannot do this too much.

15. Try past papers against the clock.

Practise writing answers in a set time. This is a good habit from the start but is especially important when you get closer to exam time.

16. Collaborate with friends.

Test each other and talk about the material – this can really help. Two brains are better than one! It is amazing how talking about a problem can help you solve it.

17. Know your weaknesses.

Ask your teacher for help to identify what you don't know. Try to do this as early as possible. If you are having trouble, it is probably with a difficult topic, so your teacher will already be aware of this – most students will find it tough.

18. Have your materials organised and ready.

Know what is needed for each exam:

- Do you need a calculator or a ruler?
- Should you have pencils as well as pens?
- Will you need water or paper tissues?

19. Make full use of school resources.

Find out what support is on offer:

- Are there study classes available?
- When is the library open?
- When is the best time to ask for extra help?
- Can you borrow textbooks, study guides, past papers, etc.?
- Is school open for Easter revision?

20. Keep fit and healthy!

Try to stick to a routine as much as possible, including with sleep. If you are tired, sluggish or dehydrated, it is difficult to see how concentration is even possible. Combine study with relaxation, drink plenty of water, eat sensibly, and get fresh air and exercise – all these things will help more than you could imagine. Good luck!

HIGHER

2018

National Qualifications 2018

X713/76/02

**Chemistry
Section 1 — Questions**

MONDAY, 21 MAY

9:00 AM — 11:30 AM

Instructions for the completion of Section 1 are given on *Page two* of your question and answer booklet X713/76/01.

Record your answers on the answer grid on *Page three* of your question and answer booklet.

You may refer to the Chemistry Data Booklet for Higher and Advanced Higher.

Before leaving the examination room you must give your question and answer booklet to the Invigilator; if you do not, you may lose all the marks for this paper.

SECTION 1 — 20 marks

Attempt ALL questions

1. The potential energy diagram below refers to the reversible reaction involving reactants **R** and products **P**.

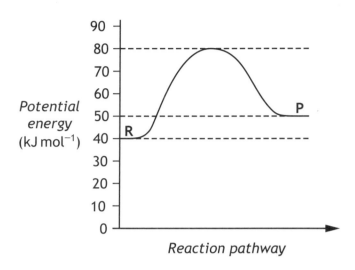

What is the enthalpy change, in $kJ\,mol^{-1}$, for the **reverse** reaction?

   A   −40

   B   −10

   C   +10

   D   +30

2. The relative rate of a reaction which reached completion in 1 minute 40 seconds is

   A $0{\cdot}010\,s^{-1}$

   B $0{\cdot}714\,s^{-1}$

   C $0{\cdot}010\,min^{-1}$

   D $0{\cdot}714\,min^{-1}$.

3.

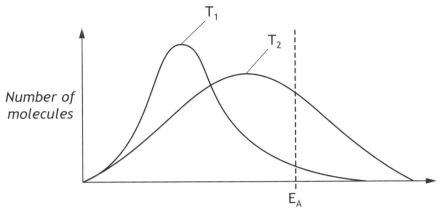

Kinetic energy of molecules

Which of the following is the correct interpretation of the above energy distribution diagram for a reaction as the temperature **decreases** from T_2 to T_1?

	Activation energy (E_A)	Number of successful collisions
A	remains the same	increases
B	decreases	decreases
C	decreases	increases
D	remains the same	decreases

4. The table shows the first three ionisation energies of aluminium.

Ionisation energy (kJ mol^{-1})		
First	Second	Third
578	1817	2745

Using this information, what is the enthalpy change, in kJ mol^{-1}, for the following reaction?

$$Al^+(g) \rightarrow Al^{3+}(g) + 2e^-$$

A   1817

B   2395

C   4562

D   5140

[Turn over

5. An element contains covalent bonding and London dispersion forces.

   The element could be

   A   boron

   B   neon

   C   sodium

   D   sulfur.

6. Erythrose is a chemical that is known to kill cancer cells.

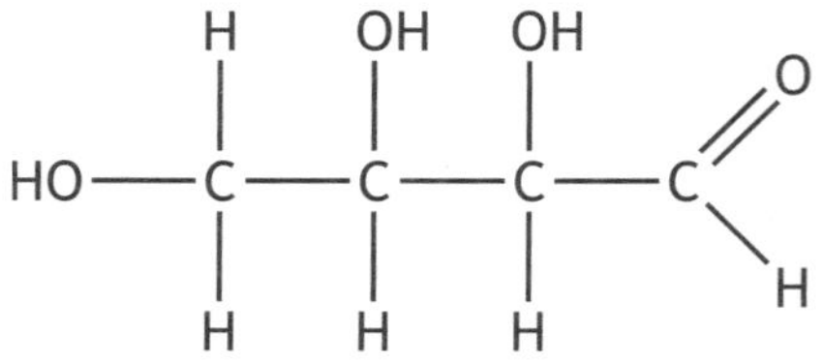

erythrose

   The two functional groups present in erythrose are

   A   carboxyl and ester

   B   carbonyl and ester

   C   carbonyl and hydroxyl

   D   carboxyl and hydroxyl.

7.

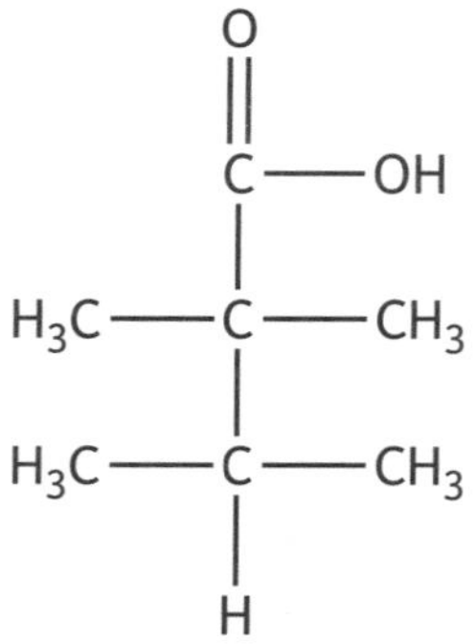

   The name of the above compound is

   A   2,2,3-trimethylbutanoic acid

   B   2,3,3-trimethylbutanoic acid

   C   1,1,2,2-tetramethylpropanoic acid

   D   2,2,3,3-tetramethylpropanoic acid.

8. Which of the following is an isomer of pentan-3-ol?

    A $CH_3CH_2CH(OH)CH_2CH_3$

    B $CH_3CHCHCH_2CH_2OH$

    C $CH_3CHCHCH(OH)CH_3$

    D $CH_3CH(CH_3)CH_2CH_2OH$

9. Oxidation of 4-methylpentan-2-ol to the corresponding ketone results in the alcohol

    A   losing 2 g per mole

    B   gaining 2 g per mole

    C   losing 16 g per mole

    D   gaining 16 g per mole.

10. Essential amino acids are defined as the amino acids which

    A   are necessary for building proteins

    B   humans must acquire through their diet

    C   plants cannot synthesise for themselves

    D   are produced when any protein is hydrolysed.

11. A mixture of carbon monoxide and hydrogen can be converted into water and a mixture of hydrocarbons.

    n CO + (2n + 1) H₂ → n H₂O + hydrocarbons

    What is the general formula for the hydrocarbons produced?

    A C_nH_{2n-2}

    B C_nH_{2n}

    C C_nH_{2n+1}

    D C_nH_{2n+2}

12. A mixture of sodium chloride and sodium sulfate is known to contain 0·6 mol of chloride ions and 0·2 mol of sulfate ions.

    How many moles of sodium ions are present?

    A   0·4

    B   0·5

    C   0·8

    D   1·0

13. Under the same conditions of temperature and pressure, which of the following gases would occupy the largest volume?

    A   0·20 g of hydrogen

    B   0·44 g of carbon dioxide

    C   0·60 g of neon

    D   0·80 g of argon

14. $3CuO + 2NH_3 \rightarrow 3Cu + N_2 + 3H_2O$

    What volume of gas, in cm^3, would be obtained by reaction between $100\,cm^3$ of ammonia gas and excess copper(II) oxide?

    All volumes are measured at atmospheric pressure and 20 °C.

    A   50

    B   100

    C   200

    D   400

15. $Cl_2(g) + H_2O(\ell) \rightleftharpoons Cl^-(aq) + ClO^-(aq) + 2H^+(aq)$

    The addition of which of the following substances would move the above equilibrium to the right?

    A   Hydrogen

    B   Hydrogen chloride

    C   Sodium chloride

    D   Sodium hydroxide

16. When 3·6 g of butanal (mass of one mole = 72 g) was burned, 124 kJ of energy was released.

    What is the enthalpy of combustion of butanal, in $kJ\,mol^{-1}$?

    A   −6·2

    B   +6·2

    C   −2480

    D   +2480

17. Consider the reaction pathways shown below.

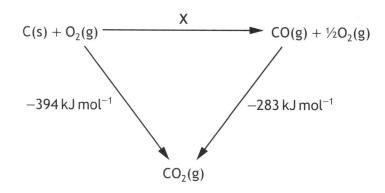

According to Hess's Law, the enthalpy change, in $kJ\,mol^{-1}$, for reaction **X** is

A   +111

B   −111

C   −677

D   +677.

18. $SO_3^{2-}(aq) + H_2O(\ell) \longrightarrow SO_4^{2-}(aq) + 2H^+(aq) + 2e^-$

Which of the following ions could be used to oxidise sulfite ions to sulfate ions?

A $Cr^{3+}(aq)$

B $Al^{3+}(aq)$

C $Fe^{3+}(aq)$

D $Sn^{4+}(aq)$

19. During a redox reaction nitrate ions, NO_3^-, are converted to nitrogen monoxide, NO.

$$NO_3^- \longrightarrow NO$$

Which line in the table correctly completes the ion-electron equation?

	Reactants	Products
A	$6H^+ + 5e^-$	$3H_2O$
B	$4H^+ + 3e^-$	$2H_2O$
C	$6H^+$	$3H_2O + 5e^-$
D	$4H^+$	$2H_2O + 3e^-$

20.

$$ICl(\ell) + Cl_2(g) \rightleftharpoons ICl_3(s) \qquad \Delta H = -106\,kJ\,mol^{-1}$$

Which line in the table identifies correctly the changes that will cause the greatest increase in the proportion of solid in the above equilibrium mixture?

	Temperature	Pressure
A	decrease	decrease
B	decrease	increase
C	increase	decrease
D	increase	increase

[END OF SECTION 1. NOW ATTEMPT THE QUESTIONS IN SECTION 2 OF YOUR QUESTION AND ANSWER BOOKLET.]

FOR OFFICIAL USE

National Qualifications 2018

Mark

X713/76/01

Chemistry
Section 1 — Answer Grid
and Section 2

MONDAY, 21 MAY

9:00 AM – 11:30 AM

Fill in these boxes and read what is printed below.

Full name of centre

Town

Forename(s)

Surname

Number of seat

Date of birth

Day   Month   Year   Scottish candidate number

Total marks — 100

SECTION 1 — 20 marks

Attempt ALL questions.

Instructions for the completion of Section 1 are given on *Page two*.

SECTION 2 — 80 marks

Attempt ALL questions.

You may refer to the Chemistry Data Booklet for Higher and Advanced Higher.

Write your answers clearly in the spaces provided in this booklet. Additional space for answers and rough work is provided at the end of this booklet. If you use this space you must clearly identify the question number you are attempting. Any rough work must be written in this booklet. You should score through your rough work when you have written your final copy.

Use **blue** or **black** ink.

Before leaving the examination room you must give this booklet to the Invigilator; if you do not, you may lose all the marks for this paper.

The questions for Section 1 are contained in the question paper X713/76/02.

Read these and record your answers on the answer grid on *Page three* opposite.

Use **blue** or **black** ink. Do NOT use gel pens or pencil.

1. The answer to each question is **either** A, B, C or D. Decide what your answer is, then fill in the appropriate bubble (see sample question below).

2. There is **only one correct** answer to each question.

3. Any rough working should be done on the additional space for answers and rough work at the end of this booklet.

Sample question

To show that the ink in a ball-pen consists of a mixture of dyes, the method of separation would be:

    A   fractional distillation

    B   chromatography

    C   fractional crystallisation

    D   filtration.

The correct answer is **B** — chromatography. The answer **B** bubble has been clearly filled in (see below).

Changing an answer

If you decide to change your answer, cancel your first answer by putting a cross through it (see below) and fill in the answer you want. The answer below has been changed to **D**.

If you then decide to change back to an answer you have already scored out, put a tick (✓) to the **right** of the answer you want, as shown below:

    or

SECTION 1 — Answer Grid

	A	B	C	D
1	○	○	○	○
2	○	○	○	○
3	○	○	○	○
4	○	○	○	○
5	○	○	○	○
6	○	○	○	○
7	○	○	○	○
8	○	○	○	○
9	○	○	○	○
10	○	○	○	○
11	○	○	○	○
12	○	○	○	○
13	○	○	○	○
14	○	○	○	○
15	○	○	○	○
16	○	○	○	○
17	○	○	○	○
18	○	○	○	○
19	○	○	○	○
20	○	○	○	○

[BLANK PAGE]

DO NOT WRITE ON THIS PAGE

[Turn over for next question

DO NOT WRITE ON THIS PAGE

MARKS | DO NOT WRITE IN THIS MARGIN

SECTION 2 — 80 marks

Attempt ALL questions

1. The elements of group 7 in the periodic table are known as the halogens.

   (a) Going down group 7 the electronegativity of the halogens decreases.

      (i) State what is meant by the term *electronegativity*.   **1**

      (ii) Explain why electronegativity values decrease going down group 7.   **1**

   (b) Explain **fully** why the boiling points of the halogens increase going down group 7.

   In your answer you should name the intermolecular forces involved.   **3**

MARKS | DO NOT WRITE IN THIS MARGIN

2. The elements sodium to argon form the third period of the periodic table.

   (a) Explain the decrease in atom size going across the third period from sodium to argon.

   1

   (b) Elements in the third period of the periodic table form chlorides.

   The structures of three of these chlorides are shown.

   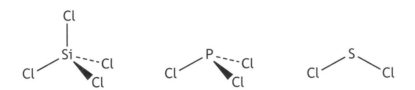

   (i) Circle the structure of the molecule above that contains **bonds** with the lowest polarity.

   (An additional diagram, if required, can be found on *Page thirty-seven.*)

   1

   (ii) Explain **fully** why, of these three chlorides, silicon tetrachloride is the most soluble in hexane.

   2

[Turn over

MARKS | DO NOT WRITE IN THIS MARGIN

2. **(continued)**

(c) Silicon tetrachloride can be used to make silicon nitride (Si_3N_4), a compound found in many cutting tools.

(i) Silicon nitride has a melting point of 1900 °C and does not conduct electricity when molten.

Explain **fully**, in terms of structure and bonding, why silicon nitride has a high melting point.

2

(ii) An equation for the formation of silicon nitride is shown.

$$3SiCl_4 \quad + \quad 16NH_3 \quad \rightarrow \quad Si_3N_4 \quad + \quad 12NH_4Cl$$

| mass of one mole = 170·1 g | mass of one mole = 17·0 g | mass of one mole = 140·3 g | mass of one mole = 53·5 g |

Calculate the atom economy for the formation of silicon nitride.

2

MARKS | DO NOT WRITE IN THIS MARGIN

2. (continued)

(d) Aluminium, another element in the third period, also forms a chloride. Aluminium chloride is prepared by reacting aluminium metal and chlorine gas.

Chlorine gas is produced by the reaction between hydrochloric acid and sodium hypochlorite. The chlorine is then passed over heated aluminium foil, forming aluminium chloride as a hot gas. The hot aluminium chloride gas and unreacted chlorine gas are passed into a flask where the aluminium chloride cools to a fine white powder.

For safety it is important that any unreacted chlorine gas can escape from the flask.

(i) Complete a labelled diagram to show an apparatus suitable for carrying out this preparation.   **2**

(An additional diagram, if required, can be found on *Page thirty-seven*).

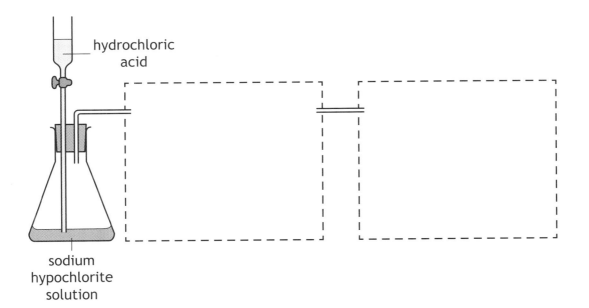

hydrochloric acid

sodium hypochlorite solution

(ii) Explain why the aluminium foil needs to be heated at the start of the preparation, despite the reaction being highly exothermic.   **1**

[Turn over

MARKS | DO NOT WRITE IN THIS MARGIN

3. Methyl benzoate is commonly added to perfumes as it has a pleasant smell.

A student carries out a reaction to produce methyl benzoate using the following apparatus.

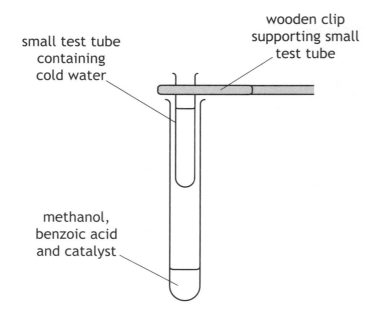

(a) The reaction mixture needs to be heated.

Describe a safe method of heating a flammable mixture.

1

(b) Suggest a reason why there is a small test tube filled with cold water in the neck of the tube containing the reaction mixture.

1

MARKS

DO NOT WRITE IN THIS MARGIN

3.   (continued)

(c)   The chemical reaction involved in the experiment is shown.

$$C_6H_5COOH(s) \quad + \quad CH_3OH(\ell) \quad \rightarrow \quad C_6H_5COOCH_3(\ell) \quad + \quad X$$

benzoic acid   methyl benzoate

mass of one   mass of one   mass of one
mole = 122 g   mole = 32 g   mole = 136 g

(i)   Name product X.   1

(ii) In a laboratory experiment, a student used 5·0 g of benzoic acid and 2·5 g of methanol to produce methyl benzoate.

Explain why benzoic acid is the limiting reactant.

You must include calculations in your answer.   2

(iii) The student produced 3·1 g of methyl benzoate from 5·0 g of benzoic acid. Benzoic acid costs £39·80 for 500 g.

Calculate the cost, in £, of the benzoic acid needed to make 100 g of methyl benzoate using the student's method.   2

MARKS

4.   3-Methylbutanal is a compound that is found in low concentrations in many types of food. The structure of 3-methylbutanal is shown.

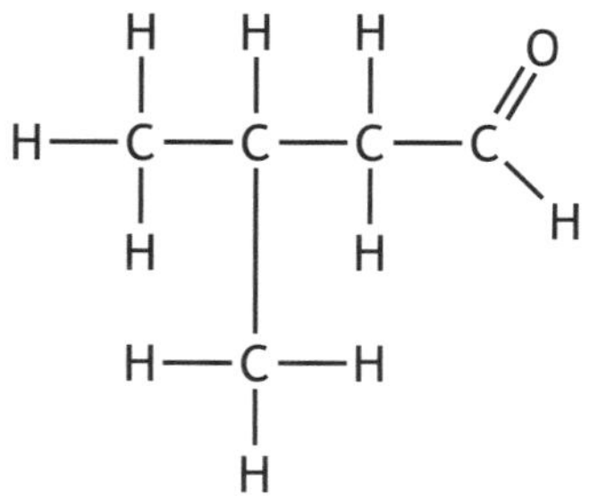

(a) Draw a structural formula for a ketone that is an isomer of 3-methylbutanal.

1

(b) Name a reagent which could be used to distinguish between 3-methylbutanal and a ketone.

1

(c) Name the strongest intermolecular force that occurs between 3-methylbutanal molecules.

1

MARKS | DO NOT WRITE IN THIS MARGIN

4. **(continued)**

(d) 3-Methylbutanal is found in olive oil.   2

Explain **fully** what can happen to 3-methylbutanal that will cause the olive oil to develop an unpleasant taste.

(e) 3-Methylbutanal can be used as a reactant in the production of other compounds. One reaction scheme involving 3-methylbutanal is shown.

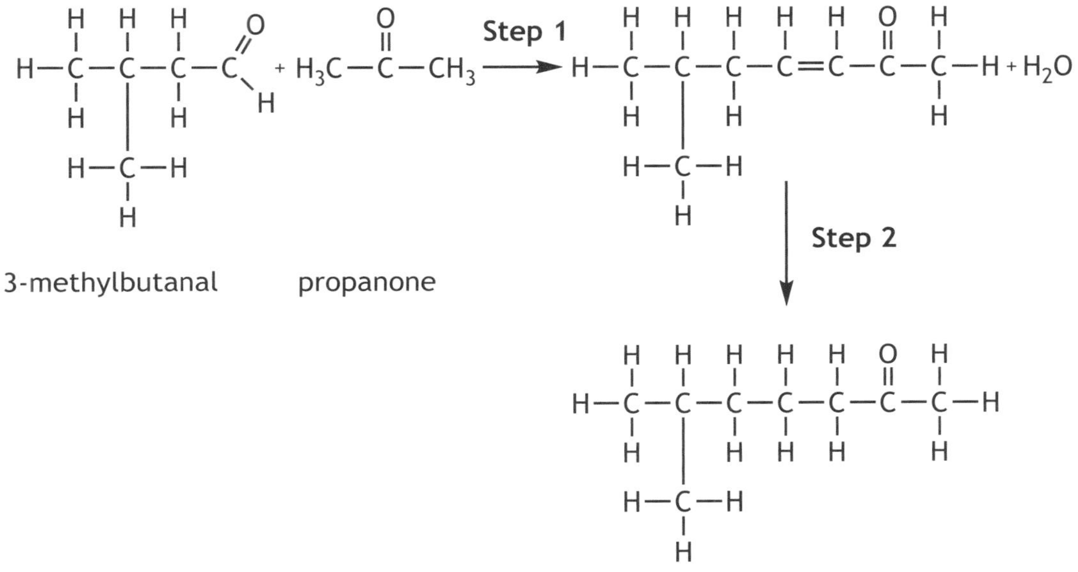

3-methylbutanal   propanone

product A

(i) Explain why **step 1** is described as a condensation reaction.   1

(ii) Give the systematic name for **product A**.   1

MARKS | DO NOT WRITE IN THIS MARGIN

5. Many chemical compounds are related to each other by their structural features, the way they are made and how they are used.

    Using your knowledge of chemistry, describe the relationships between fats, oils, detergents, soaps and emulsifiers.

3

[Turn over for next question

DO NOT WRITE ON THIS PAGE

6. Skin creams contain many different chemicals.

    (a) Retinol (vitamin A) promotes cell regeneration.

         One method of supplying retinol to the skin is by using a skin cream containing the compound retinyl palmitate.

$$C_{15}H_{31} - \overset{\overset{\displaystyle O}{\|}}{C} - O - C_{20}H_{29}$$

retinyl palmitate

         Retinyl palmitate is absorbed into the skin and then broken down to form retinol.

         (i) Name the type of reaction that occurs when retinyl palmitate is broken down to form retinol.

         1

         (ii) Write a molecular formula for retinol.

         1

    (b) Skin creams often contain vitamin E to prevent damage to the skin caused by free radicals.

         (i) Describe how free radicals are formed.

         1

6. (b) (continued)

(ii) Hydroxyl free radicals ($\cdot$OH) can attack fatty acids present in cell membranes. One step in the chain reaction is shown below.

$C_{18}H_{31}O_2$ + $\cdot$OH $\rightarrow$ $C_{18}H_{30}O_2\cdot$ + H_2O

State the name given to this step in the chain reaction.   **1**

(iii) The antioxidant vitamin E is a free radical scavenger.

State how free radical scavengers prevent further chain reactions.   **1**

[Turn over

6. **(continued)**

(c) Palmitoyl pentapeptide-4 is also used in skin creams.

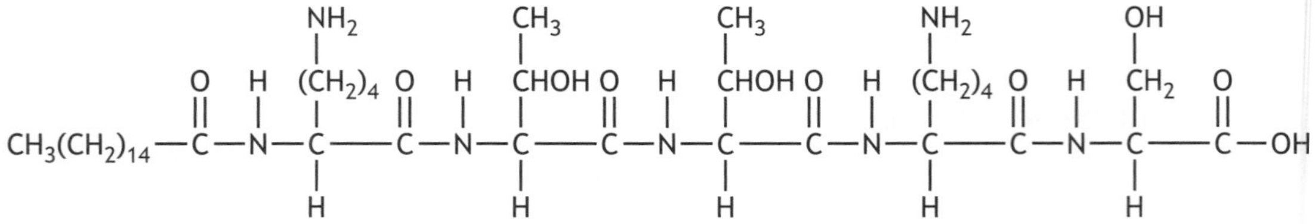

(i) Circle a peptide link in the above structure.

(An additional diagram, if required, can be found on *Page thirty-seven*.)

1

(ii) Palmitoyl pentapeptide-4 is formed from palmitic acid and three different amino acids.

Molecule	Number of molecules used to form one molecule of palmitoyl pentapeptide-4
palmitic acid	1
threonine	2
serine	1
lysine	2

Draw a structural formula for the amino acid serine.

1

7. Terpenes consist of joined isoprene units (2-methylbuta-1,3-diene). They are classified by the number of isoprene units in the molecule.

Class of terpene	Number of isoprene units
hemiterpene	1
monoterpene	2
sesquiterpene	3
diterpene	4
triterpene	6

(a) Myrcene and humulene are terpenes present in hops which give beer its characteristic flavour and aroma.

(i) Circle an isoprene unit on the myrcene structure below.   **1**

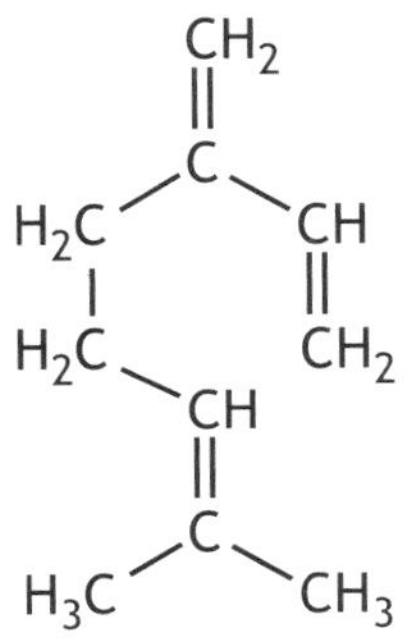

$$CH_2$$
$$\|$$
$$C$$
$$H_2C \quad CH$$
$$| \quad \|$$
$$H_2C \quad CH_2$$
$$CH$$
$$\|$$
$$C$$
$$H_3C \quad CH_3$$

(An additional diagram, if required, can be found on *Page thirty-eight*.)

(ii) Humulene has the molecular formula $C_{15}H_{24}$.

Name the class of terpene to which humulene belongs.   **1**

[Turn over

MARKS | DO NOT WRITE IN THIS MARGIN

7. **(continued)**

(b) (i) Squalene, a triterpene, is included in some flu vaccines to enhance the body's immune response. A single dose of flu vaccine contains 10·69 mg of squalene.

Calculate the mass of squalene required to produce a batch of 500 000 doses of flu vaccine.

Your answer must be given in kg.

2

(ii) Squalane is a fully saturated hydrocarbon used in skin moisturising cream.

Squalane can be made by the reaction of squalene with hydrogen.

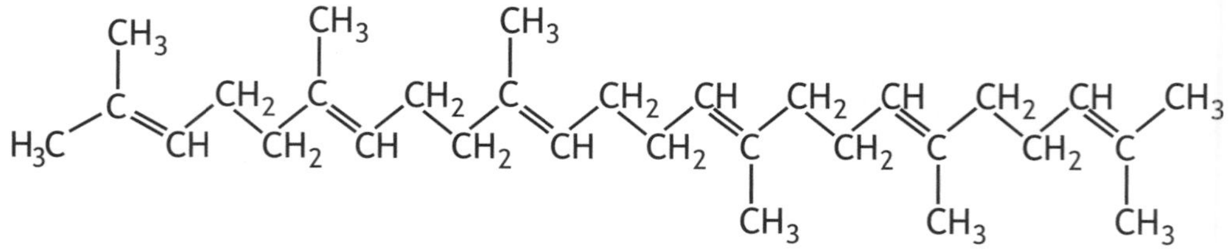

squalene

State the number of moles of hydrogen needed to fully saturate one mole of squalene to produce one mole of squalane.

1

7. (continued)

(c) The monoterpene limonene, found in lemon oil, can be converted into the alcohol, terpineol.

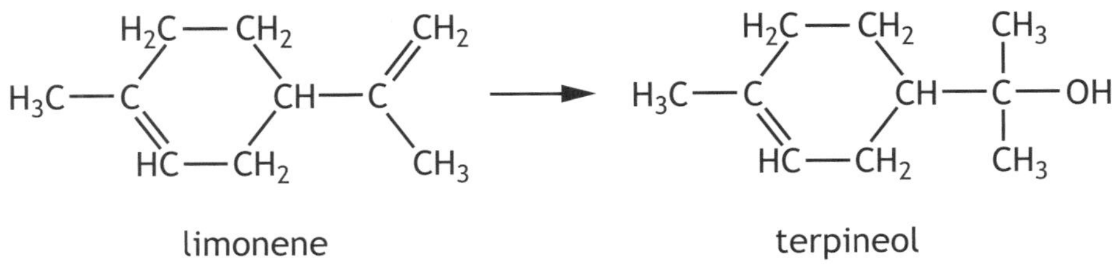

limonene   terpineol

(i) Name the type of reaction taking place.   **1**

(ii) When terpineol is heated with copper(II) oxide, no reaction takes place.

Explain why no reaction takes place.   **1**

[Turn over

MARKS | DO NOT WRITE IN THIS MARGIN

8. The alkynes are a homologous family of hydrocarbons.

   (a) The simplest member of the family is ethyne, C_2H_2, used in welding torches.

$$H-C\equiv C-H$$

Ethyne can be produced from ethane.

Using bond enthalpies and mean bond enthalpies from the data book, calculate the enthalpy change, in $kJ\,mol^{-1}$, for this reaction.

2

   (b) Hess's Law can be used to calculate the enthalpy change for reactions that do not normally take place, such as the formation of propyne from its elements.

$$3C(s) \quad + \quad 2H_2(g) \quad \rightarrow \quad C_3H_4(g)$$

Calculate the enthalpy change, in $kJ\,mol^{-1}$, for this reaction using the following information.

2

$$C(s) + O_2(g) \quad \rightarrow \quad CO_2(g) \qquad \Delta H = -394\,kJ\,mol^{-1}$$

$$H_2(g) + \tfrac{1}{2}O_2(g) \quad \rightarrow \quad H_2O(\ell) \qquad \Delta H = -286\,kJ\,mol^{-1}$$

$$C_3H_4(g) + 4O_2(g) \quad \rightarrow \quad 3CO_2(g) + 2H_2O(\ell) \qquad \Delta H = -1939\,kJ\,mol^{-1}$$

MARKS | DO NOT WRITE IN THIS MARGIN

8.   (continued)

(c) Propyne, C_3H_4 (1 mole = 40 g), has been suggested as a possible rocket fuel.

(i)   The enthalpy of combustion of propyne is $-1939\,kJ\,mol^{-1}$.

Calculate the energy released, in kJ, when 1 kg of propyne is burned completely.

1

(ii)   The mass of air required to burn 1 g of fuel can be calculated using the relationship shown.

Mass of air, in g = 4·3 × mass of oxygen, in g, for complete combustion of 1 g of fuel

Calculate the mass of air, in g, required to burn 1 g of propyne.

2

$$C_3H_4(g) \quad + \quad 4O_2(g) \quad \rightarrow \quad 3CO_2(g) \quad + \quad 2H_2O(\ell)$$

MARKS | DO NOT WRITE IN THIS MARGIN

8. (c) (continued)

(iii) The table shows the mass of air required to burn 1 g of different fuels.

Fuel	Mass of 1 mole (g)	Mass of air required to burn 1 g
ethane	30	16·1
propane	44	15·6
methanol	32	6·5
ethanol	46	9·0

Suggest why methanol and ethanol, compared to the other fuels, require less air to burn 1 g.

1

[Turn over for next question

DO NOT WRITE ON THIS PAGE

MARKS | DO NOT WRITE IN THIS MARGIN

9.   Ethane-1,2-diol can be made from ethene.

(a)   The flow chart of an industrial process to produce ethane-1,2-diol is shown.

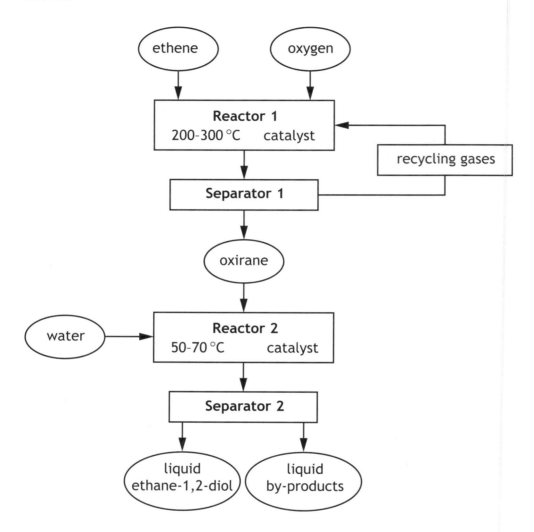

(i)   Industrial processes are designed to maximise profit.

Using the flowchart, suggest two ways to maximise profit in this industrial process.

2

MARKS | DO NOT WRITE IN THIS MARGIN

9. (a) (continued)

    (ii) Name the process used in **Separator 2** to separate ethane-1,2-diol from the larger liquid by-products.   **1**

  (b) Explain fully why ethane-1,2-diol is more viscous than propan-1-ol.   **2**

  (c) Draw a structural formula for a diol that contains three carbon atoms.   **1**

[Turn over

MARKS | DO NOT WRITE IN THIS MARGIN

9. **(continued)**

(d) Ethane-1,2-diol has been found to be harmful to animals. Treatment for affected animals involves using a 20% ethanol solution.

    (i) The 20% ethanol solution is prepared by accurately measuring 20 cm^3 of ethanol and then making up to exactly 100 cm^3 with water.

       Describe the procedure which should be used to prepare 100 cm^3 of the 20% ethanol solution.

2

    (ii) An affected animal must be treated with 9 doses of 20% ethanol solution. Each dose contains 5 cm^3 of the ethanol solution for every kilogram body mass of the animal.

       Calculate the total volume, in cm^3, of the 20% ethanol solution needed to treat a 3·5 kg animal.

1

MARKS | DO NOT WRITE IN THIS MARGIN

9. (d) (continued)

(iii) Ethane-1,2-diol is harmful because it is oxidised in the body to form glycolic acid.

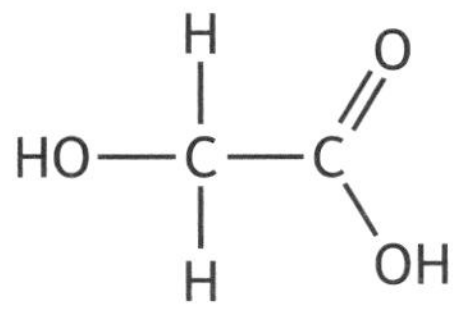

glycolic acid

(A) Draw a structural formula for another possible product of oxidation of ethane-1,2-diol.　　1

(B) Glycolic acid can be neutralised by sodium hydroxide to form sodium glycolate.

Give a formula for sodium glycolate.　　1

[Turn over

MARKS DO NOT WRITE IN THIS MARGIN

10. The molar volume (in units of litres per mole) is the same for all gases at the same temperature and pressure.

    Using your knowledge of chemistry, suggest how the molar volume of gases could be measured and compared. Any suitable chemicals and apparatus can be used. Some suggested chemicals and apparatus are given below.

3

Chemicals	Apparatus
hydrochloric acid	gas syringe
zinc	measuring cylinder
magnesium	delivery tube
calcium	stoppers
water	$500 \, cm^3$ flask
sodium carbonate	vacuum pump
calcium carbonate	balance
cylinder of nitrogen	cork ring
cylinder of hydrogen	burette
cylinder of carbon dioxide	filter funnel

10. **(continued)**

[Turn over

MARKS

11. Iodine is required for a healthy diet. Food grown in certain parts of the world is low in iodine. To prevent iodine deficiency in people's diets, table salt can be 'iodised' by the addition of very small quantities of potassium iodide, KI.

The number of moles of iodide in a sample of salt can be determined by the following procedure.

Step 1

Prepare a standard salt solution by dissolving an accurately weighed sample of iodised salt (50·0 g) in water to give a final volume of 250 cm^3.

Step 2

Transfer 50 cm^3 of salt solution to a conical flask and add excess bromine solution to convert the iodide ions to iodine.

Step 3

Titrate the iodine (I_2) released with sodium thiosulfate solution ($Na_2S_2O_3$).

(a) Describe a procedure to accurately weigh out a 50·0 g sample of iodised table salt.　1

(b) The overall equation for the reaction of bromine solution with iodide ions is shown.

$$2I^-(aq) \ + \ Br_2(aq) \ \longrightarrow \ I_2(aq) \ + \ 2Br^-(aq)$$

Write the ion-electron equation for the oxidation reaction.　1

MARKS | DO NOT WRITE IN THIS MARGIN

11. (continued)

(c) Three samples were prepared as described in **step 2**. Each sample was titrated with $0.0010 \, mol \, l^{-1}$ sodium thiosulfate solution.

The results are shown below.

Sample	Volume of sodium thiosulfate (cm^3)
1	10·0
2	9·4
3	9·6

(i) Calculate the average volume, in cm^3, of sodium thiosulfate solution that should be used to determine the number of moles of iodine released.

1

(ii) Calculate the number of moles of iodine released from $50 \, cm^3$ of the standard salt solution.

2

$$I_2(aq) \; + \; 2Na_2S_2O_3(aq) \; \longrightarrow \; 2NaI(aq) \; + \; Na_2S_4O_6(aq)$$

[Turn over

12. Many modern antiseptics are based on phenol. The table shows the germ-killing power of some phenol compounds.

(a)

Compound	Structure	Germ-killing power (relative to phenol)
phenol		1·0
4-methylphenol		2·5
2-chlorophenol		3·6
4-ethylphenol		7·5
2,4-dichlorophenol		13·0
4-propylphenol		20·0
2,4,6-trichlorophenol		23·0

12. (a) (continued)

    (i) Suggest two ways in which structural features increase germ-killing power of phenol compounds.

        2

    (ii) The names of the phenol compounds in the table are derived from their structures using the following rules.

        Phenol is used as the parent name for the compound.

        1. The –OH functional group is assigned as being on carbon 1 of the ring.

        2. The ring can be numbered clockwise or anticlockwise to assign numbers to the other atoms or groups. The numbers should be assigned so that the lowest possible numbers are used.

        3. If two or more identical atoms or groups are present, use one of the prefixes di, tri or tetra.

        4. The names of the atoms or groups attached to the ring are listed alphabetically (ignoring the prefixes for alphabetical purposes).

        Using these rules, name this molecule.

        1

[Turn over

MARKS | DO NOT WRITE IN THIS MARGIN

12. (continued)

(b) There are different methods of producing phenol.

(i) In the early 1900s, phenol was produced by the following reaction.

$$C_6H_6 \ + \ H_2SO_4 \ + \ 2NaOH \ \rightarrow \ C_6H_5OH \ + \ Na_2SO_3 \ + \ 2H_2O$$

benzene   phenol

mass of   mass of
one mole   one mole
$= 78 \cdot 0 \, g$ $= 94 \cdot 0 \, g$

Calculate the mass of phenol, in kg, produced from 117 kg of benzene if the percentage yield is 90%.

2

(ii) Phenol is now usually produced by the Cumene Process.

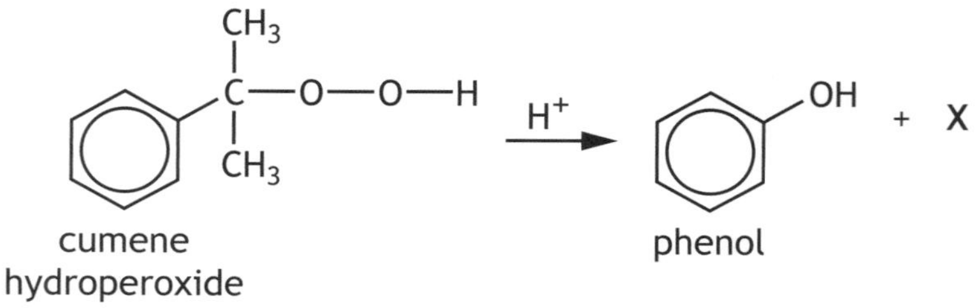

cumene
hydroperoxide

phenol

Name the other product, X, formed in the Cumene Process.

1

[END OF QUESTION PAPER]

ADDITIONAL SPACE FOR ANSWERS AND ROUGH WORK

ADDITIONAL DIAGRAM FOR USE IN QUESTION 2 (b)

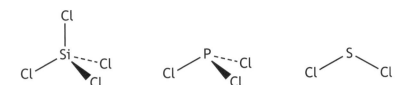

ADDITIONAL DIAGRAM FOR USE IN QUESTION 2 (d) (i)

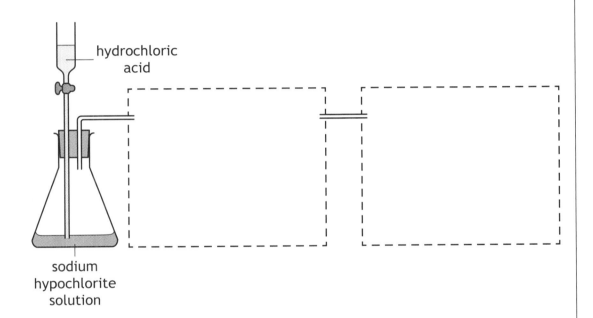

ADDITIONAL DIAGRAM FOR USE IN QUESTION 6 (c) (i)

$CH_3(CH_2)_{14}$—C—N—C—C—N—C—C—N—C—C—N—C—C—N—C—C—OH

ADDITIONAL SPACE FOR ANSWERS AND ROUGH WORK

ADDITIONAL DIAGRAM FOR USE IN QUESTION 7 (a) (i)

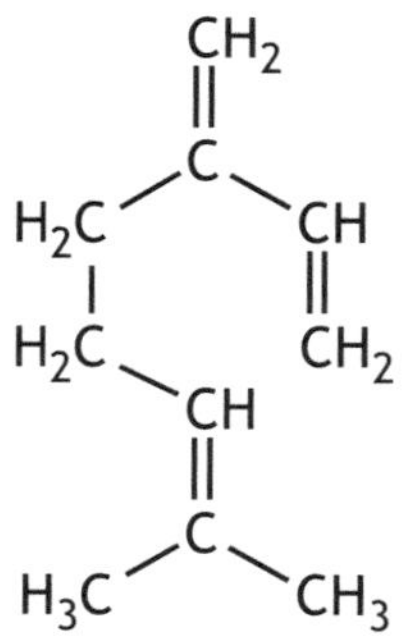

$$CH_2$$
$$\|$$
$$C$$
$$H_2C \qquad CH$$
$$| \qquad \|$$
$$H_2C \qquad CH_2$$
$$CH$$
$$\|$$
$$C$$
$$H_3C \qquad CH_3$$

MARKS | DO NOT WRITE IN THIS MARGIN

ADDITIONAL SPACE FOR ANSWERS AND ROUGH WORK

ADDITIONAL SPACE FOR ANSWERS AND ROUGH WORK

Page forty

2018 Specimen Question Paper

National
Qualifications
SPECIMEN ONLY

S813/76/12

Chemistry
Paper 1 — Multiple choice

Date — Not applicable

Duration — 40 minutes

Total marks — 25

Attempt ALL questions.

You may use a calculator.

Instructions for the completion of Paper 1 are given on *Page two* of your answer booklet S813/76/02.

Record your answers on the answer grid on *Page three* of your answer booklet.

You may refer to the Chemistry Data Booklet for Higher and Advanced Higher.

Space for rough work is provided at the end of this booklet.

Before leaving the examination room you must give your answer booklet to the Invigilator; if you do not, you may lose all the marks for this paper.

Total marks — 25

Attempt ALL questions

1. Which of the following elements, at room temperature, could be described as monatomic?

   A   Argon

   B   Boron

   C   Iodine

   D   Sulfur

2. The table shows the first three ionisation energies of aluminium.

Ionisation energy (kJ mol^{-1})		
1st	2nd	3rd
578	1817	2745

   Using this information, what is the enthalpy change, in kJ mol^{-1}, for the following reaction?

   $$Al^{3+}(g) + 2e^- \rightarrow Al^+(g)$$

   A   +2167

   B   −2167

   C   +4562

   D   −4562

3. Which element has the greatest attraction for bonding electrons?

   A   Bromine

   B   Chlorine

   C   Lithium

   D   Sodium

4. Which of the following chlorides is likely to have the most ionic character?

   A $BeCl_2$

   B $CaCl_2$

   C $CsCl$

   D $LiCl$

5. Which of the following elements would have the strongest London dispersion forces?

   A   Argon

   B   Chlorine

   C   Nitrogen

   D   Oxygen

6. The shapes of some common molecules are shown below and each contains at least one polar bond.

   Which molecule is non-polar?

   A   H—Cl

   B

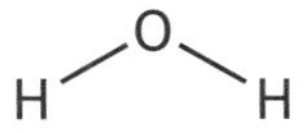

   C   O=C=O

   D

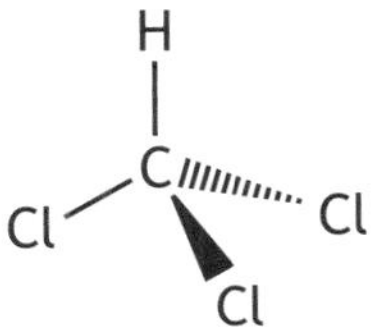

7. Which of the following is an isomer of hexan-2-ol?

   A CH_3—CH_2—CH_2—CH_2—CH—OH
                                    |
                                    CH_3

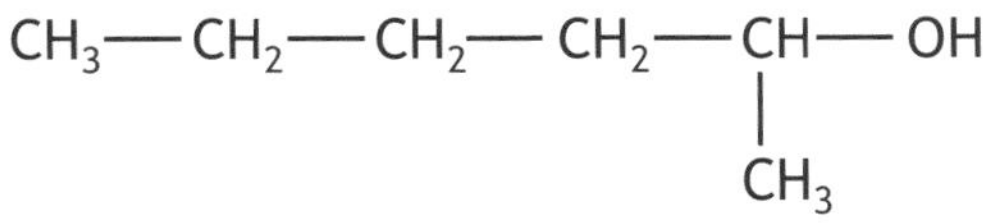

   B

   C CH_3—CH —CH_2—CH_2—CH_2—CH_3
              |
              OH

   D CH_3—CH_2—CH—CH—CH_3
                     | |
                     CH_3 OH

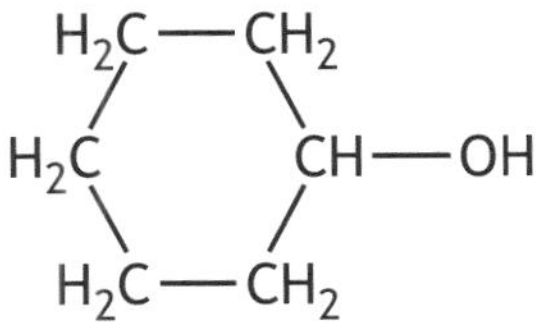

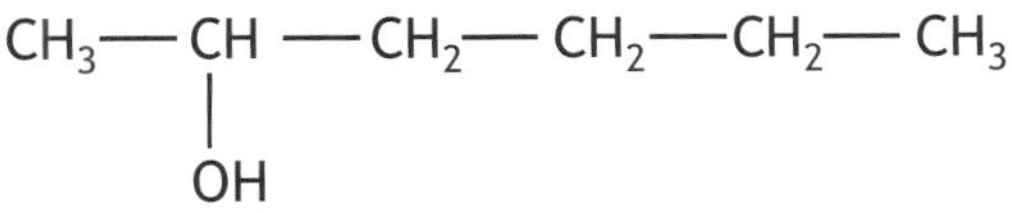

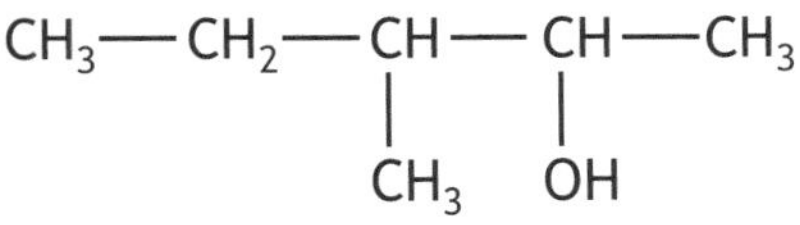

[Turn over

8. Aspirin and oil of wintergreen are used in medicine. Their structures are shown below.

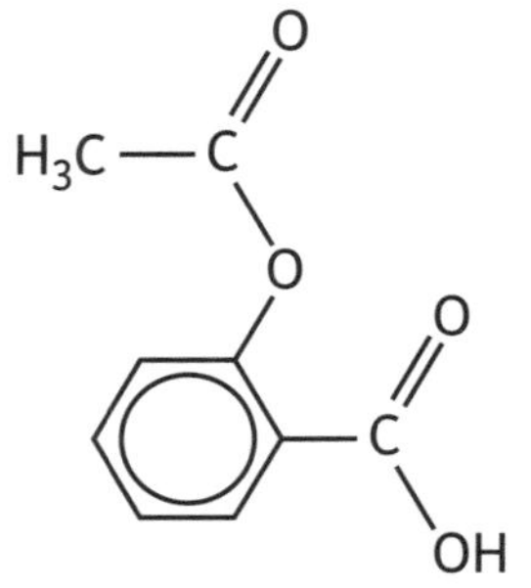

aspirin 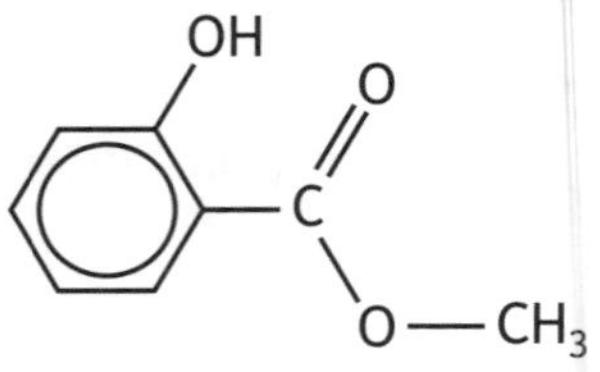   oil of wintergreen

Identify the term which can be applied to aspirin but **not** to oil of wintergreen.

A   Aldehyde

B   Ketone

C   Ester

D   Carboxylic acid

9. The structure of caryophyllene, which can be extracted from clove oil, is

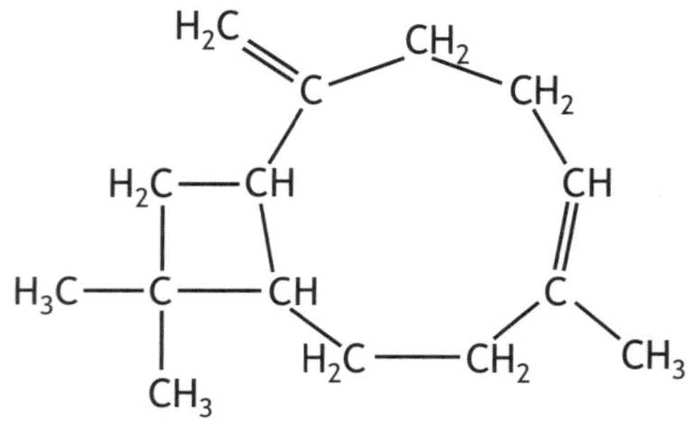

Which of the following would be the best solvent for extracting caryophyllene?

A CH_3—CH_2—CH_2—CH_2—CH_2—CH_3

B CH_3—CH_2—CH_2—CH_2—CH_2—CHO

C CH_3—CH_2—CH_2—CO—CH_2—CH_3

D   HO—CH_2—CH_2—CH_2—CH_2—CH_2—CH_3

10. In α-amino acids the amino group is on the carbon atom next to the carboxyl group.

Which of the following is an α-amino acid?

A H_3C—CH—COOH
           |
          H_2C—NH_2

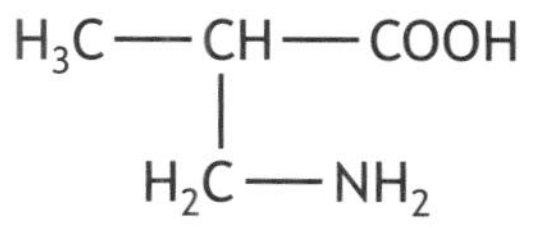

B H_2C—CH—COOH
         | |
        SH NH_2

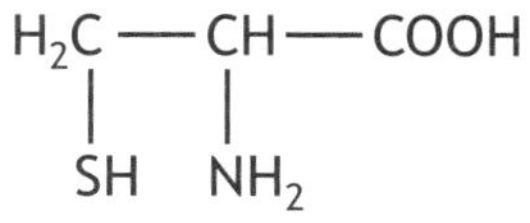

C

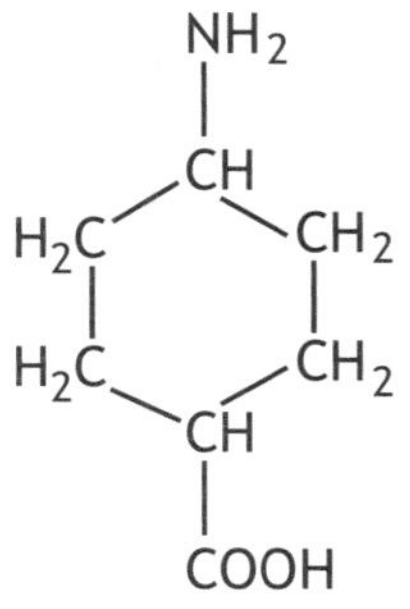

             NH_2
             |
           CH
     H_2C CH_2
       |
     H_2C CH_2
         CH
          |
         COOH

D

             NH_2
             |
          CH
     H_2C CH_2
       |
     H_2C CH
        CH_2 COOH

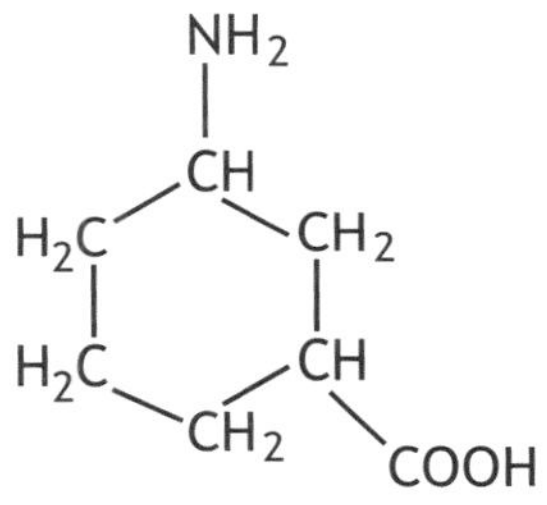

[Turn over

11. The 2-pyrones are esters used as flavourings and in perfumes. The name '2-pyrone' comes from the carbonyl group being in position **2** in the structure shown.

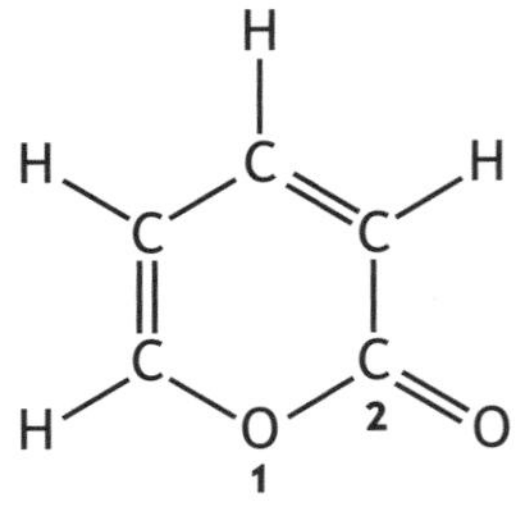

Which of the following structures is the pyrone responsible for the smell of chocolate, 4-hydroxy-6-methyl-2-pyrone?

A

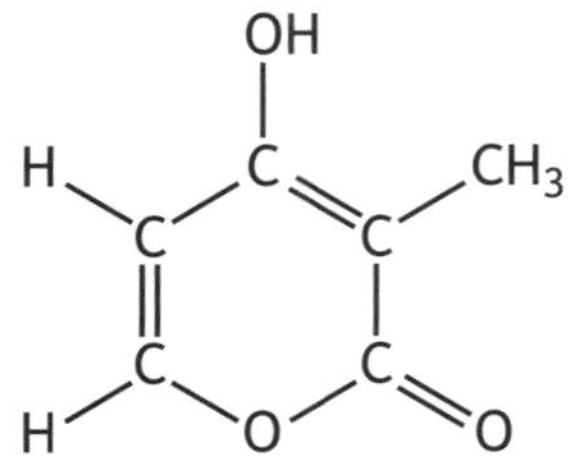

B

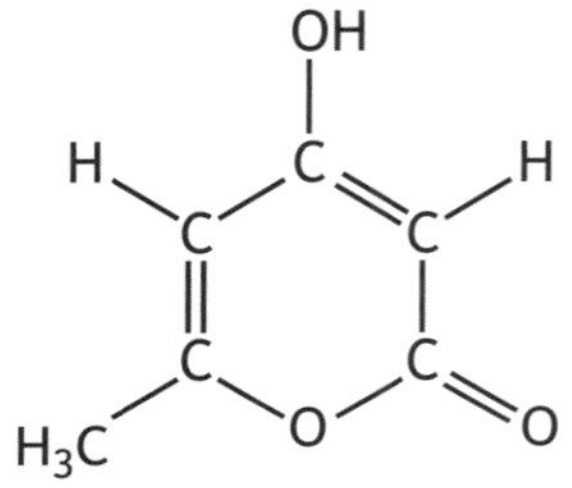

C

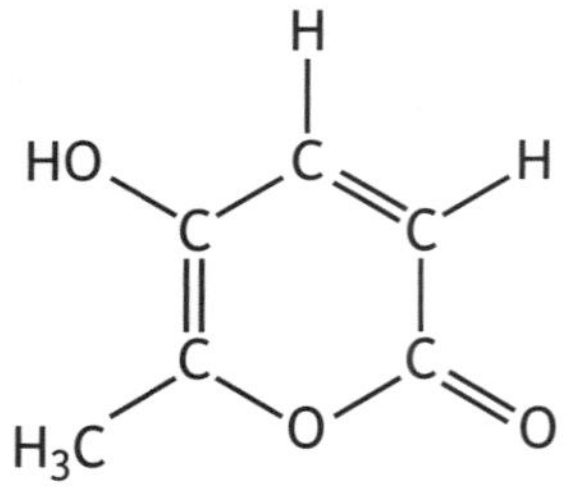

D

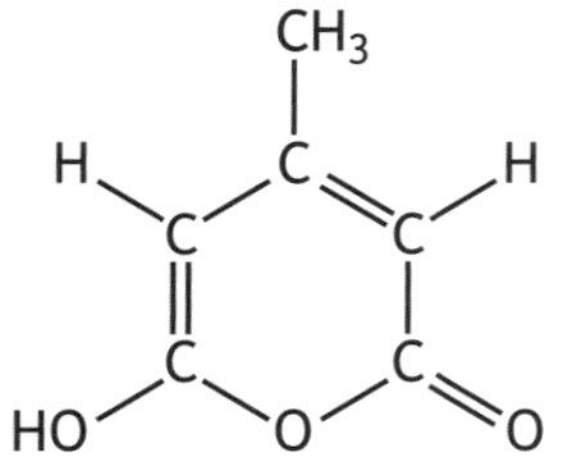

12. Which of the following reactions can be classified as reduction?

    A CH_3CH_2OH $\rightarrow$ CH_3COOH

    B $CH_3CH(OH)CH_3$ $\rightarrow$ CH_3COCH_3

    C $CH_3CH_2COCH_3$ $\rightarrow$ $CH_3CH_2CH(OH)CH_3$

    D CH_3CH_2CHO $\rightarrow$ CH_3CH_2COOH

13. Which of the following structural formulae represents a tertiary alcohol?

    A

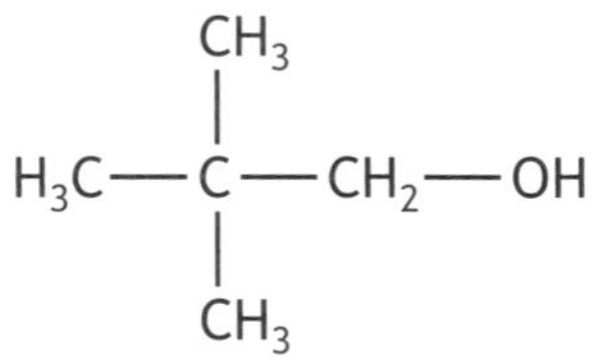

    B

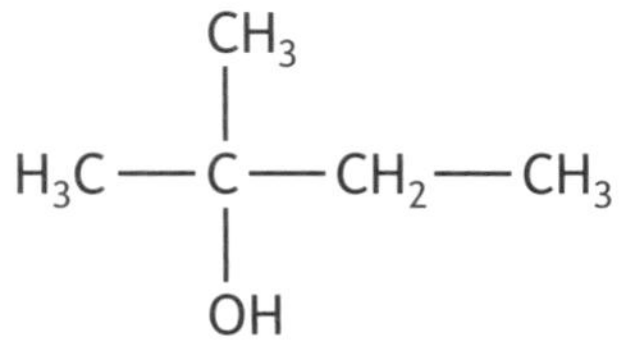

    C

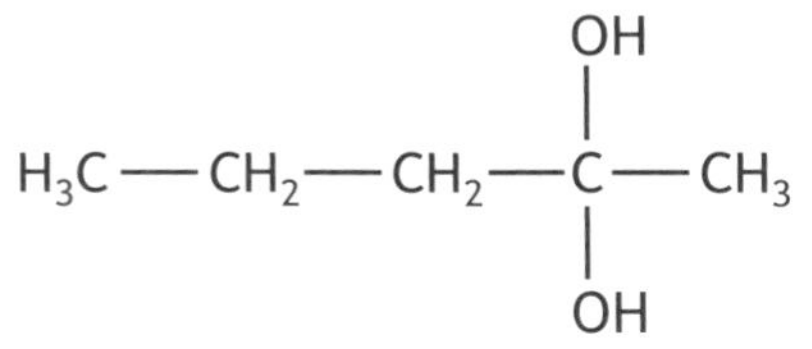

    D

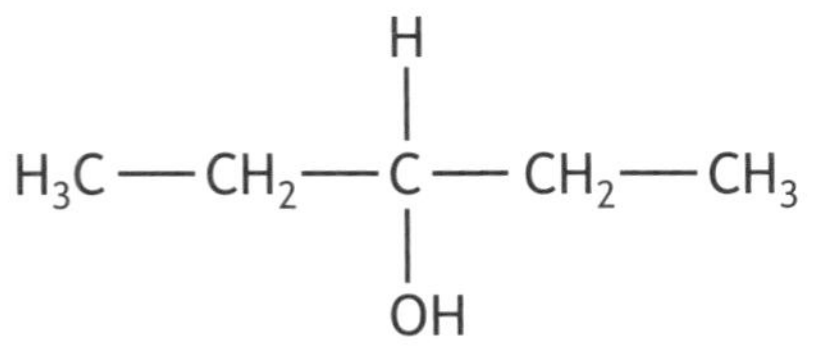

[Turn over

14. A mixture of sodium bromide and sodium sulfate is known to contain 10 moles of sodium and 4 moles of bromide ions.

    How many moles of sulfate ions are present?

    A   3

    B   4

    C   5

    D   6

15. 4·6 g of sodium is added to 4·8 litres of oxygen to form sodium oxide.

    When the reaction is complete, which of the following statements will be true?

    (Take the volume of 1 mole of oxygen to be 24 litres.)

    A   0·10 mol of oxygen will be left unreacted.

    B   0·10 mol of sodium will be left unreacted.

    C   0·15 mol of oxygen will be left unreacted.

    D   0·20 mol of sodium oxide will be formed.

16. A student obtained a certain volume of carbon dioxide by the reaction of $20\,cm^3$ of $2\,mol\,l^{-1}$ hydrochloric acid, HCl, with excess sodium carbonate.

    $$2HCl(aq) \;+\; Na_2CO_3(aq) \;\longrightarrow\; 2NaCl(aq) \;+\; CO_2(g) \;+\; H_2O(\ell)$$

    The student carried out a similar experiment using sulfuric acid, H_2SO_4.

    $$H_2SO_4(aq) \;+\; Na_2CO_3(aq) \;\longrightarrow\; Na_2SO_4(aq) \;+\; CO_2(g) \;+\; H_2O(\ell)$$

    Which solution of sulfuric acid would give the same final volume of carbon dioxide when added to excess sodium carbonate?

    A $10\,cm^3$ of $2\,mol\,l^{-1}$

    B $20\,cm^3$ of $2\,mol\,l^{-1}$

    C $10\,cm^3$ of $4\,mol\,l^{-1}$

    D $20\,cm^3$ of $4\,mol\,l^{-1}$

17. In a reversible reaction, equilibrium is reached when

    A   molecules of reactants stop changing into molecules of products

    B   the concentrations of reactants and products are equal

    C   the concentrations of reactants and products are constant

    D   the activation energy of the forward reaction is equal to that of the reverse reaction.

18. Ethanol is manufactured by reacting ethene with steam.

$$C_2H_4(g) \; + \; H_2O(g) \; \rightleftharpoons \; C_2H_5OH(g) \qquad \Delta H = -46\,kJ\,mol^{-1}$$

    Which set of conditions would give the best yield of ethanol at equilibrium?

    A   High temperature, low pressure

    B   High temperature, high pressure

    C   Low temperature, high pressure

    D   Low temperature, low pressure

19. When copper carbonate is reacted with excess acid, carbon dioxide is produced.
    The curves shown were obtained under different conditions.

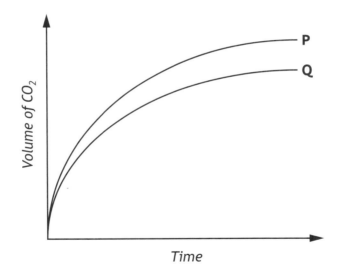

    The change from **P** to **Q** could be brought about by

    A   increasing the concentration of the acid

    B   decreasing the mass of copper carbonate

    C   decreasing the particle size of the copper carbonate

    D   adding a catalyst.

[Turn over

20. The potential energy diagram for a reaction is shown.

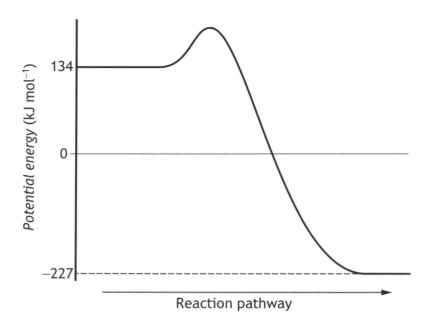

ΔH, in kJ mol^{-1}, for the forward reaction is

A   +361

B   −93

C   −227

D   −361

21. Which of the following is **not** a correct statement about the effect of a catalyst?
The catalyst

A   provides energy so that more molecules have successful collisions

B   lowers the energy that molecules need for successful collisions

C   provides an alternative route to the products

D   allows more molecules to have energies greater than the activation energy.

22. Which of the following equations represents an enthalpy of combustion?

A $C_2H_6(g)$ + $3\frac{1}{2}O_2(g)$ $\rightarrow$ $2CO_2(g)$ + $3H_2O(\ell)$

B $C_2H_5OH(\ell)$ + $O_2(g)$ $\rightarrow$ $CH_3COOH(\ell)$ + $H_2O(\ell)$

C $CH_3CHO(\ell)$ + $\frac{1}{2}O_2(g)$ $\rightarrow$ $CH_3COOH(\ell)$

D $CH_4(g)$ + $1\frac{1}{2}O_2(g)$ $\rightarrow$ $CO(g)$ + $2H_2O(\ell)$

23. $5N_2O_4(\ell) + 4CH_3NHNH_2(\ell) \rightarrow 4CO_2(g) + 12H_2O(\ell) + 9N_2(g)$ $\Delta H = -5116\,kJ$

The energy released when 2 moles of each reactant are mixed and ignited is

A   2046 kJ

B   2558 kJ

C   4093 kJ

D   5116 kJ.

[Turn over

24. A chemist analysed a mixture of four dyes **A**, **B**, **C** and **D** using gas-liquid chromatography.

In this technique, compounds are separated depending on their polarity, with the most polar having the longest retention times. The chromatogram obtained is shown below.

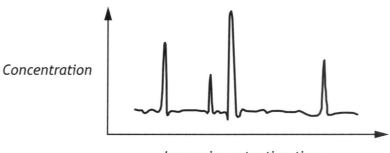

Concentration

Increasing retention time

Which of the following compounds was present in greatest concentration?

Dye	Structure
A	
B	
C	
D	

25. Ethanol and ethanoic acid are flammable liquids.

Which of the following diagrams shows the correct set up for the separation of ethanol from ethanoic acid?

A

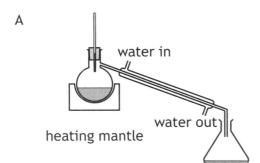

B

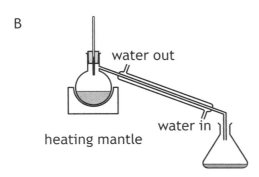

C

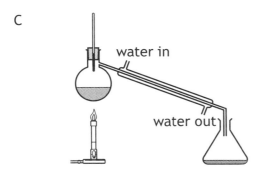

D

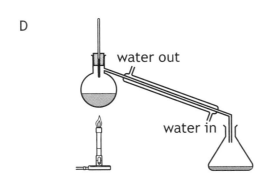

[END OF SPECIMEN QUESTION PAPER]

SPACE FOR ROUGH WORK

H

National Qualifications
SPECIMEN ONLY

Mark

S813/76/02

Chemistry
Paper 1 — Multiple choice
Answer booklet

Date — Not applicable

Duration — 40 minutes

Fill in these boxes and read what is printed below.

Full name of centre

Town

Forename(s)

Surname

Number of seat

Date of birth
Day   Month   Year   Scottish candidate number

Instructions for the completion of Paper 1 are given on *Page two*.

Record your answers on the answer grid on *Page three*.

Use **blue** or **black** ink.

Before leaving the examination room you must give your answer booklet to the Invigilator; if you do not, you may lose all the marks for this paper.

Paper 1 — 25 marks

The questions for Paper 1 are contained in the question paper S813/76/12.

Read these and record your answers on the answer grid on *Page three*.

Use **blue** or **black** ink. Do NOT use gel pens or pencil.

1. The answer to each question is **either** A, B, C or D. Decide what your answer is, then fill in the appropriate bubble (see sample question below).

2. There is **only one correct** answer to each question.

3. Any rough working should be done on the space for rough work at the end of the question paper S813/76/12.

Sample question

To show that the ink in a ball-pen consists of a mixture of dyes, the method of separation would be:

    A   fractional distillation

    B   chromatography

    C   fractional crystallisation

    D   filtration.

The correct answer is **B** — chromatography. The answer **B** bubble has been clearly filled in (see below).

Changing an answer

If you decide to change your answer, cancel your first answer by putting a cross through it (see below) and fill in the answer you want. The answer below has been changed to **D**.

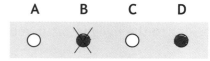

If you then decide to change back to an answer you have already scored out, put a tick (✓) to the **right** of the answer you want, as shown below:

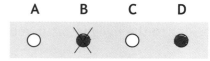

Paper 1 — Answer Grid

	A	B	C	D
1	○	○	○	○
2	○	○	○	○
3	○	○	○	○
4	○	○	○	○
5	○	○	○	○
6	○	○	○	○
7	○	○	○	○
8	○	○	○	○
9	○	○	○	○
10	○	○	○	○
11	○	○	○	○
12	○	○	○	○
13	○	○	○	○
14	○	○	○	○
15	○	○	○	○
16	○	○	○	○
17	○	○	○	○
18	○	○	○	○
19	○	○	○	○
20	○	○	○	○
21	○	○	○	○
22	○	○	○	○
23	○	○	○	○
24	○	○	○	○
25	○	○	○	○

[BLANK PAGE]

DO NOT WRITE ON THIS PAGE

H

National
Qualifications
SPECIMEN ONLY

Mark

S813/76/01

**Chemistry
Paper 2**

Date — Not applicable

Duration — 2 hours 20 minutes

Fill in these boxes and read what is printed below.

Full name of centre

Town

Forename(s)

Surname

Number of seat

Date of birth

Day	Month	Year	Scottish candidate number

Total marks — 95

Attempt ALL questions.

You may use a calculator.

You may refer to the Chemistry Data Booklet for Higher and Advanced Higher.

Write your answers clearly in the spaces provided in this booklet. Additional space for answers and rough work is provided at the end of this booklet. If you use this space you must clearly identify the question number you are attempting. Any rough work must be written in this booklet. Score through your rough work when you have written your final copy.

Use **blue** or **black** ink.

Before leaving the examination room you must give this booklet to the Invigilator; if you do not, you may lose all the marks for this paper.

MARKS | DO NOT WRITE IN THIS MARGIN

Total marks — 95

Attempt ALL questions

1. The periodic table allows chemists to make predictions about the properties of elements.

(a) The elements lithium to neon make up the second period of the periodic table.

Li	Be	B	C	N	O	F	Ne

(i) Name an element from the second period that can exist as a covalent network. **1**

(ii) Explain why the atoms decrease in size from lithium to neon. **1**

(iii) Name the element that is the strongest reducing agent in the second period. **1**

MARKS | DO NOT WRITE IN THIS MARGIN

1. **(continued)**

(b) On descending group 1 from lithium to caesium, the electronegativity of the elements decreases.

Explain **fully** why the electronegativity of the elements decreases going down group 1.

2

(c) Tin(IV) iodide is a compound formed from a metal element and a non-metal element.

Tin(IV) iodide is a bright orange powder that dissolves easily in non-polar solvents. It has a melting point of 143 °C and a boiling point of 340 °C.

Name the type of bonding **and** structure present in tin(IV) iodide.

1

[Turn over

MARKS | DO NOT WRITE IN THIS MARGIN

2. The table below contains information about some diatomic molecules.

	H—H	H—Cl	Cl—Cl	I—Cl	Br—Br
Boiling point (°C)	−253	−85	−34	97	59
Bond enthalpy ($kJ\,mol^{-1}$)	436	432	243	211	194

(a) Boiling points can be used to show the effect of intermolecular forces.

Explain **fully** why ICl and Br_2 provide good evidence for a fair comparison of the relative strengths of different types of intermolecular force. 3

(b) State which of the diatomic molecules listed in the table above has the strongest covalent bond. 1

2. **(continued)**

(c) Hydrogen and chlorine gases were used in an experiment to demonstrate a free radical reaction.

A test-tube was wrapped with black tape leaving a 'window' on one side. The tube was filled with a mixture of hydrogen and chlorine. When a bright light was directed at the tube, the gas mixture exploded and the ball was fired across the room.

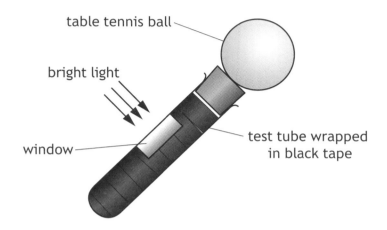

table tennis ball

bright light

window

test tube wrapped in black tape

A free radical chain reaction is initiated when light energy causes chlorine radicals to form as shown below.

$$\text{Initiation} \quad \text{Cl—Cl} \xrightarrow{\text{light}} \text{Cl} \cdot \ + \ \text{Cl} \cdot$$

(i) Complete the equations below showing possible propagation and termination steps. **2**

$$\text{Propagation} \quad \text{Cl} \cdot \ + \ \text{H—H} \longrightarrow \qquad +$$

$$\text{Termination} \quad \text{H} \cdot \ + \ \text{H} \cdot \longrightarrow$$

(ii) Suggest why the test tube was wrapped in black tape. **1**

[Turn over

2. (c) **(continued)**

(iii) When hydrogen gas and chlorine gas react hydrogen chloride gas is produced.

$$H_2(g) \ + \ Cl_2(g) \ \rightarrow \ 2HCl(g)$$

Using bond enthalpy values, calculate the enthalpy change, in $kJ\,mol^{-1}$, for the reaction of one mole of hydrogen with one mole of chlorine.

2

(d) Chlorine can be made in a redox reaction between permanganate ions and chloride ions.

The ion-electron equations for the oxidation and reduction reactions are shown below.

$$2Cl^-(aq) \ \rightarrow \ Cl_2(g) \ + \ 2e^-$$

$$MnO_4^-(aq) \ + \ 8H^+(aq) \ + \ 5e^- \ \rightarrow \ Mn^{2+}(aq) \ + \ 4H_2O(\ell)$$

Write a balanced equation for the reaction of permanganate ions with chloride ions to produce chlorine gas.

1

MARKS | DO NOT WRITE IN THIS MARGIN

3. A team of chemists are developing a shower gel.

    (a) A suitable fragrance must be created for the shower gel.

        (i) To give the gel a fruity smell the chemists are considering adding an ester. They synthesise six isomeric esters. Volunteers smell each ester and give it a rating out of one hundred depending on how fruity the smell is.

Structure	Fruit-smell rating
CH_3-C (=O) $O-CH_2-CH_2-CH_2-CH_2-CH_3$	100
CH_3-C (=O) $O-CH-CH_2-CH_2-CH_3$ with CH_3 branch	34
CH_3-C (=O) $O-C(CH_3)(CH_3)-CH_2-CH_3$	0
CH_3-CH_2-C (=O) $O-CH_2-CH_2-CH_2-CH_3$	92
$CH_3-CH(CH_3)-C$ (=O) $O-CH_2-CH_2-CH_3$	44
$CH_3-C(CH_3)(CH_3)-C$ (=O) $O-CH_2-CH_3$	32

        (A) Name the ester with the fruit-smell rating of 92.   1

[Turn over

DO NOT WRITE IN THIS MARGIN

3. **(a) (i) (continued)**

(B) Shown below are the structures of three more isomers.

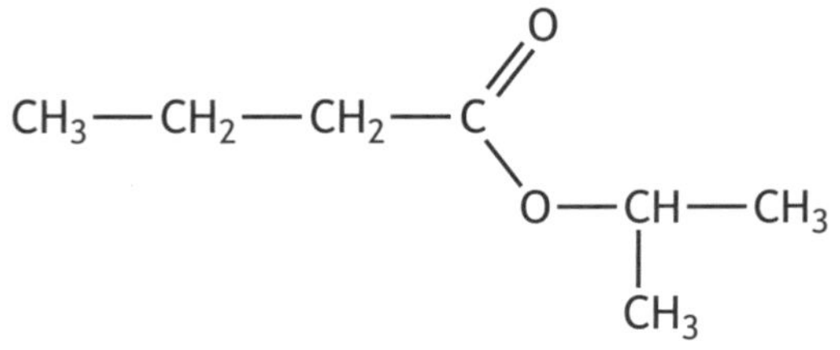

CH_3—CH_2—CH_2—C(=O)O—CH—CH_3 with CH_3 branch

Ester **A**

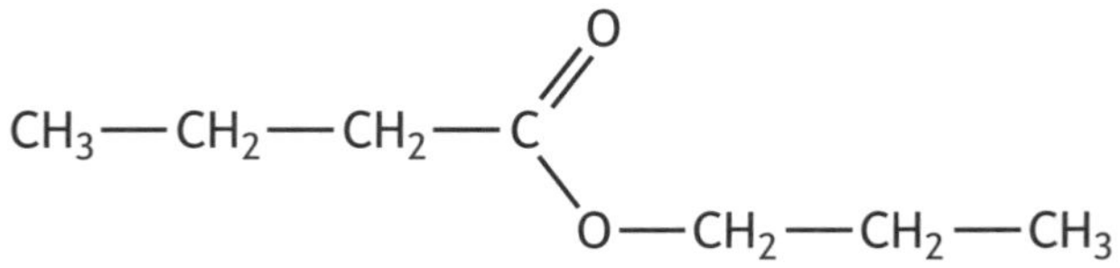

CH_3—CH_2—CH_2—C(=O)O—CH_2—CH_2—CH_3

Ester **B**

CH_3—CH_2—C(=O)O—C(CH_3)(CH_3)—CH_3

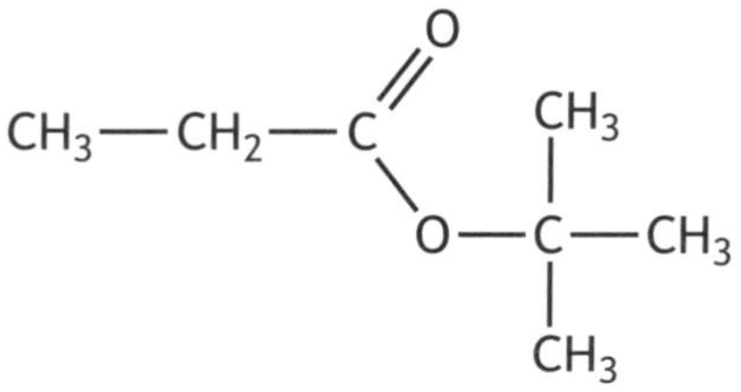

Ester **C**

Arrange these esters in order of **decreasing** fruit-smell rating. 1

Ester ☐ > Ester ☐ > Ester ☐

MARKS | DO NOT WRITE IN THIS MARGIN

3. (a) (continued)

(ii) The compound civetone will also be used in the fragrance.

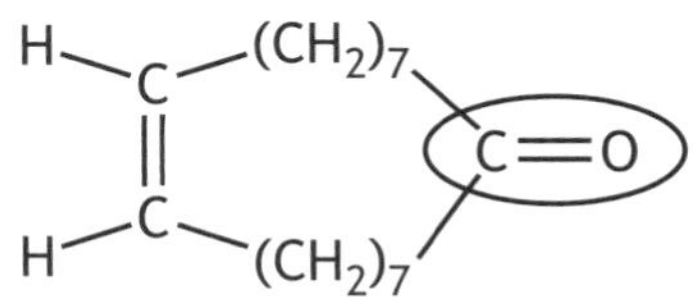

civetone

(A) Name the functional group circled in the structure above.   **1**

(B) Draw a structural formula for the alcohol that can be oxidised to form civetone.   **1**

(b) To make the shower gel produce a cold, tingling sensation when applied to the skin, menthol is added.

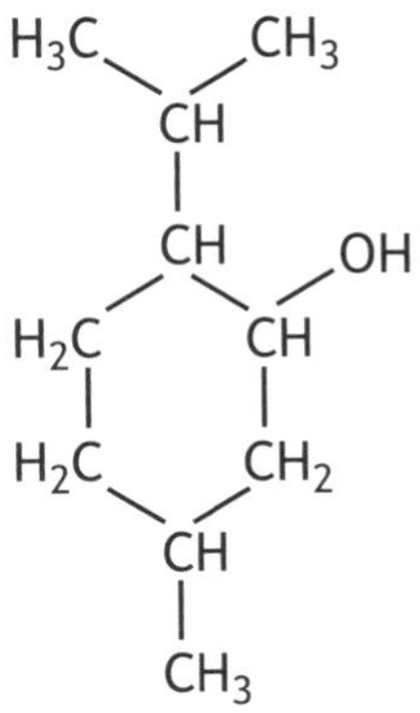

Menthol is based on two isoprene units.

Circle one of the isoprene units on the menthol structure above.   **1**

(An additional diagram, if required, can be found on *Page thirty-eight*.)

[Turn over

3. **(continued)**

(c) Sodium lauryl sulfate, a detergent, is used in the shower gel to give the product cleaning properties.

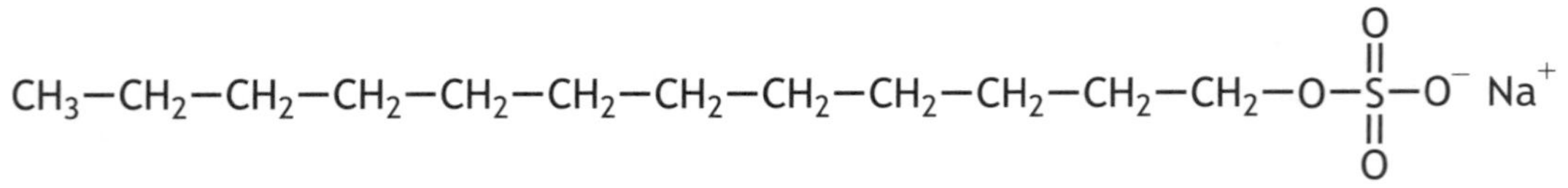

$$CH_3-CH_2-CH_2-CH_2-CH_2-CH_2-CH_2-CH_2-CH_2-CH_2-CH_2-CH_2-O-\overset{\displaystyle O}{\underset{\displaystyle O}{\overset{\|}{\underset{\|}{S}}}}-O^-\ Na^+$$

(i) **Explain fully** the cleaning action of sodium lauryl sulfate.

(You may wish to use diagrams to illustrate your answer.)

3

(ii) Explain why detergents, like sodium lauryl sulfate, are preferable to soap in hard water areas.

1

MARKS DO NOT WRITE IN THIS MARGIN

3. (continued)

(d) Esters and terpenes have been used for thousands of years to create fragrances.

Traces of liquid were discovered in a perfume bottle that belonged to Queen Hatshepsut, ruler of Egypt, over 3500 years ago.

Egyptian perfumes were made by dissolving plant extracts containing pleasant-smelling terpenes and esters in an edible oil. A little ethanol and water may also have been added.

Using your knowledge of chemistry, comment on the possible smell(s) when such a bottle is opened after being stored for thousands of years. 3

[Turn over

DO NOT WRITE IN THIS MARGIN

4.   A student carried out some experiments using different edible fats and edible oils.

(a)   The first experiment allowed the iodine number to be determined. The larger the iodine number, the greater the number of carbon-to-carbon double bonds present in the fat or oil.

Fat or oil	Iodine number	Typical molecule found in fat or oil
Olive oil	86	
Shea butter	57	
Linseed oil	173	
Sunflower oil		

MARKS | DO NOT WRITE IN THIS MARGIN

4. (a) (continued)

(i) Shea butter has the highest melting point of these substances.

Explain **fully** why the melting point of shea butter is higher than the edible oils. 3

(ii) By considering the number of carbon-to-carbon double bonds in each structure, predict the iodine number of sunflower oil. 1

[Turn over

4.   (continued)

(b) In the second experiment, soap was made by heating triolein obtained from olive oil with sodium hydroxide solution.

$$(C_{17}H_{33}COO)_3C_3H_5 \ + \ 3NaOH \ \rightarrow \ 3C_{17}H_{33}COONa \ + \ X$$

triolein   soap
GFM = 884 g   GFM = 304 g

(i) Name product X.   1

(ii) 5·00 g of triolein produced 1·28 g of soap.

Calculate the percentage yield.   3

5. Butan-2-ol is widely used as a solvent.

(a) In industry butan-2-ol is produced by the hydration of but-2-ene.

$$C_4H_8(g) \ + \ H_2O(g) \ \rightarrow \ C_4H_{10}O(g)$$

but-2-ene　　　　　　　　butan-2-ol

The enthalpy values for the following reactions are:

$$4C(s) \ + \ 4H_2(g) \ \rightarrow \ C_4H_8(g) \qquad \Delta H = \ -7.1 \, kJ \, mol^{-1}$$

$$4C(s) \ + \ 5H_2(g) \ + \ \tfrac{1}{2}O_2(g) \ \rightarrow \ C_4H_{10}O(g) \qquad \Delta H = -292.8 \, kJ \, mol^{-1}$$

$$H_2(g) \ + \ \tfrac{1}{2}O_2(g) \ \rightarrow \ H_2O(g) \qquad \Delta H = -241.8 \, kJ \, mol^{-1}$$

Using the data above, calculate the enthalpy change, in $kJ \, mol^{-1}$, for the production of butan-2-ol by hydration of but-2-ene.　　2

[Turn over

MARKS | DO NOT WRITE IN THIS MARGIN

5. **(continued)**

(b) A chemist investigated the costs invotlved in producing butan-2-ol from propanal using a two-step process.

Step One

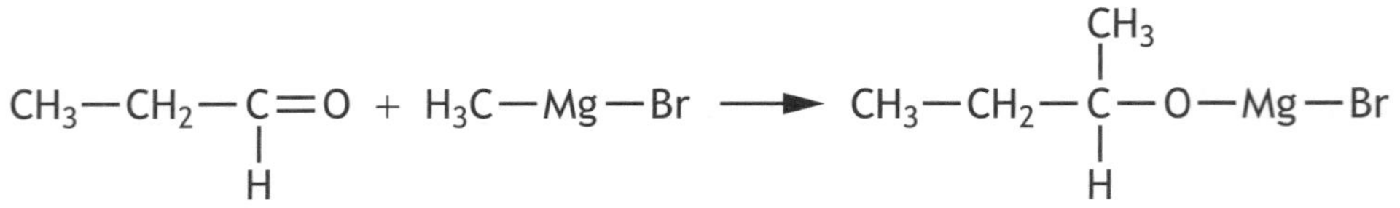

$$CH_3-CH_2-\underset{\underset{H}{|}}{C}=O + H_3C-Mg-Br \longrightarrow CH_3-CH_2-\underset{\underset{H}{|}}{\overset{\overset{CH_3}{|}}{C}}-O-Mg-Br$$

propanal   methyl magnesium bromide

Step Two

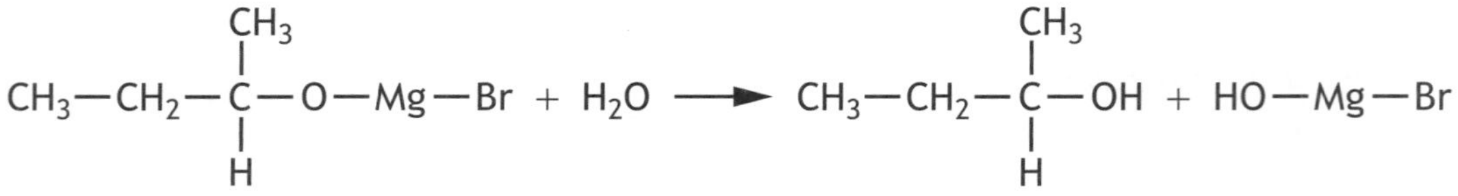

$$CH_3-CH_2-\underset{\underset{H}{|}}{\overset{\overset{CH_3}{|}}{C}}-O-Mg-Br + H_2O \longrightarrow CH_3-CH_2-\underset{\underset{H}{|}}{\overset{\overset{CH_3}{|}}{C}}-OH + HO-Mg-Br$$

butan-2-ol

(i) The chemist made 5·75 g of butan-2-ol using 5·01 g of propanal and 20·0 g of methyl magnesium bromide.

The costs of the chemicals used are shown below.

Propanal	£22·10 for 1 kg
Methyl magnesium bromide	£75·00 for 25 g

Calculate the cost of the chemicals, in £, needed to produce 100 g of butan-2-ol using this method.

2

(ii) This method can be used to produce different alcohols by using other aldehydes in place of propanal.

Name the alcohol produced if this method is repeated using pentanal.

1

MARKS | DO NOT WRITE IN THIS MARGIN

5. **(continued)**

(c) Butan-2-ol can be converted into butanone, another useful solvent.

(i) Name the type of reaction that takes place when butan-2-ol is converted into butanone. **1**

(ii) Care must be taken when using butanone as a solvent because it is highly flammable.

The lowest temperature at which butanone will ignite is called its flash point.

For the family of compounds containing butanone, the flash point can be predicted from the number of carbon atoms it contains using the formula:

flash point in °C $=$ $(14 \times$ number of carbon atoms$)$ $-$ 59

Calculate the flash point, in °C, for butanone. **1**

[Turn over

MARKS | DO NOT WRITE IN THIS MARGIN

6. Chemists have developed cheeses specifically for use in cheeseburgers.

(a) When ordinary cheese is heated, the texture changes as the protein molecules change shape.

Explain fully why protein molecules change shape when they are heated.   **2**

(b) To make cheese for burgers, ordinary cheese, soluble milk proteins and water are mixed and heated to no more than 82 °C. As the cheese begins to melt, trisodium citrate is added.

(i) Suggest why a water bath was used to heat the mixture.   **1**

(ii) Trisodium citrate is the salt formed when citric acid is neutralised using a base.

$$H_2C - COOH$$
$$|$$
$$HO - C - COOH$$
$$|$$
$$H_2C - COOH$$

citric acid

Suggest the name of a base that could be used to neutralise citric acid forming trisodium citrate.   **1**

MARKS | DO NOT WRITE IN THIS MARGIN

6. (b) (continued)

(iii) A section of the structure of a soluble milk protein is shown below.

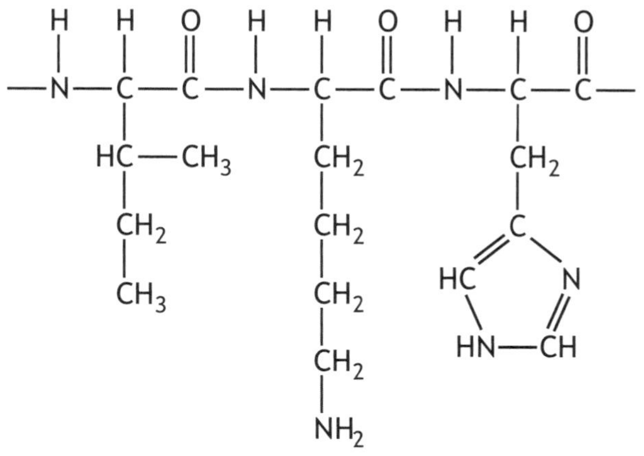

Draw a structural formula for any **one** of the amino acids formed when this section of protein is hydrolysed.

1

(c) Cheese is a source of zinc, an essential element for the body.

The mass of zinc in four 100 g samples taken from a burger cheese was measured.

Sample	Mass of zinc (mg)
1	4·0
2	21·7
3	3·9
4	4·1

Calculate the average mass of zinc, in mg, in 100 g of this burger cheese.

1

MARKS | DO NOT WRITE IN THIS MARGIN

6. **(continued)**

(d) A calorie-free replacement for the fat in cheese can be made by reacting fatty acids with the hydroxyl groups on a molecule of sucrose.

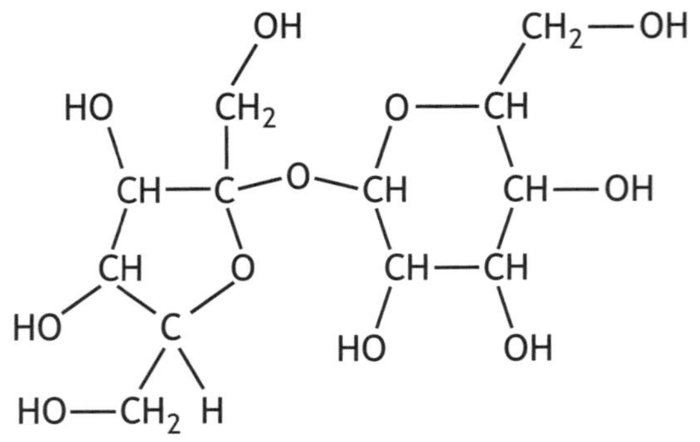

sucrose

State how many fatty acid molecules can react with one molecule of sucrose.

1

MARKS | DO NOT WRITE IN THIS MARGIN

7. Ibuprofen is one of the best-selling painkillers in the UK.

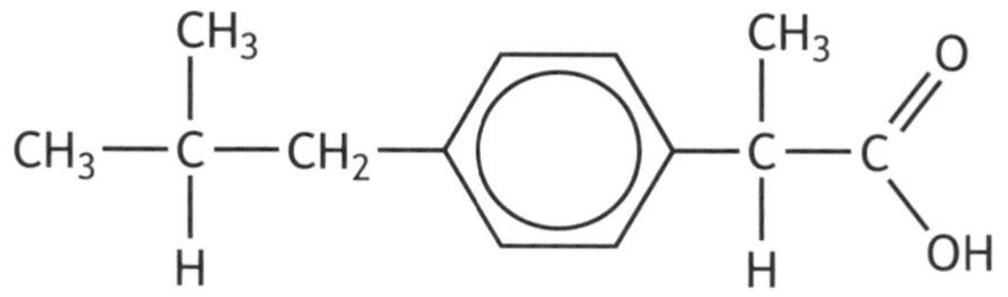

ibuprofen

(a) Ibuprofen tablets should not be taken by people who suffer from acid indigestion.

Name the functional group present in ibuprofen that makes this drug unsuitable for these people.　　　**1**

(b) From the 1990s, ibuprofen has been synthesised by a three step process.

The equation below shows the final step of the synthesis.

$$C_{12}H_{17}OH \quad + \quad CO \quad \xrightarrow{\text{Pd catalyst}} \quad C_{12}H_{17}COOH$$

ibuprofen

(i) State the percentage atom economy of this step.　　　**1**

[Turn over

7. **(b)** **(continued)**

(ii) The diagram below represents the changing potential energy during this reaction when it is carried out without the palladium catalyst.

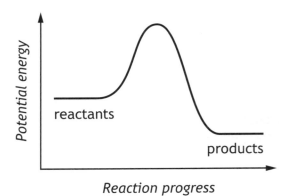

Add a line to the diagram showing the changing potential energy when the catalyst is used.

1

(An additional diagram, if required, can be found on *Page thirty-eight*.)

(c) Ibuprofen, $C_{12}H_{17}COOH$, is taken for the relief of pain in the form of pills or tablets because it is only slightly soluble in water.

(i) Suggest why ibuprofen is only slightly soluble in water.

1

MARKS | DO NOT WRITE IN THIS MARGIN

7. **(c) (continued)**

(ii) Small children can find it difficult to swallow tablets or pills so ibuprofen is supplied as an 'infant formula' liquid.

(A) The 'infant formula' also contains polysorbate 80. Its structure is shown below.

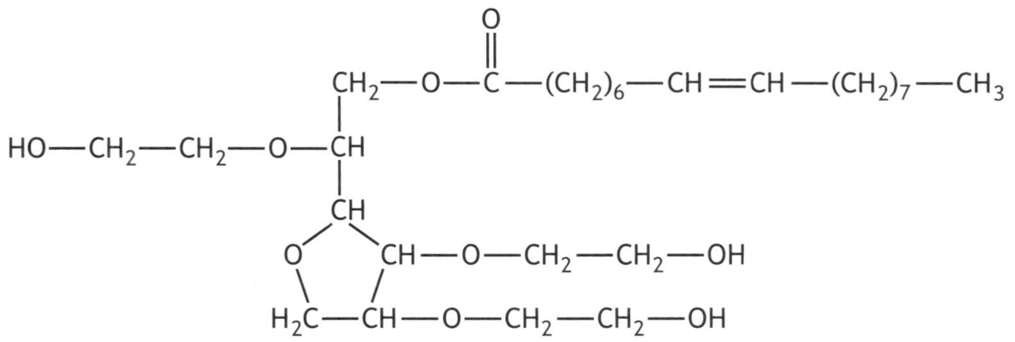

Suggest why polysorbate 80 is included in the 'infant formula'. **1**

(B) The 'infant formula' contains $2 \cdot 0$ g of ibuprofen in every $100 \, cm^3$ of liquid.

The recommended dose for treating a 6-month-old baby is $0 \cdot 050$ g.

Calculate the volume, in cm^3, of 'infant formula' needed to treat a 6-month-old baby. **1**

[Turn over

MARKS | DO NOT WRITE IN THIS MARGIN

8. Ethanol and 2-methylpropan-1-ol are alcohols that can be used as renewable fuels in car engines.

   (a) Alcohols tends to absorb water from the air causing corrosion in fuel tanks and engines. Water is absorbed because alcohols can form hydrogen bonds with water molecules.

   In the box below, showing a molecule of ethanol, draw a molecule of water and use a dotted line to show where a hydrogen bond exists between the two molecules.

   1

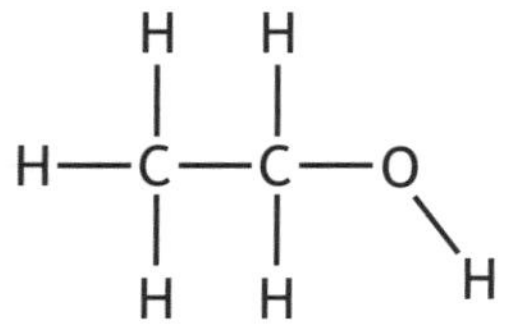

   (An additional diagram, if required, can be found on *Page thirty-eight*.)

   (b) Draw a structural formula for 2-methylpropan-1-ol.

   1

MARKS | DO NOT WRITE IN THIS MARGIN

8. **(continued)**

(c) A car was fuelled with 15 litres of ethanol. The ethanol burned releasing 351 000 kJ of energy.

Volume of 1 g of 2-methylpropan-1-ol	$1 \cdot 25 \, cm^3$
Energy released when 1 g of 2-methylpropan-1-ol burns	$36 \cdot 1 \, kJ$

Use the data in the table to calculate the volume of 2-methylpropan-1-ol that would burn to release the same quantity of energy.

3

[Turn over

MARKS | DO NOT WRITE IN THIS MARGIN

9. A student carried out an investigation to measure the fluoride and nitrite levels in a water supply.

   (a) The student prepared a set of sodium fluoride solutions of known concentration by diluting a standard solution.

      (i) State what is meant by the term **standard solution**.   1

      (ii) Calculate the mass, in mg, of sodium fluoride, NaF, needed to make 1 litre of standard solution with a **fluoride ion** concentration of $100\,mg\,l^{-1}$.   2

      (iii) Describe how the standard solution would be prepared from the weighed sample of sodium fluoride.   3

      (iv) Suggest why the student should use distilled or deionised water rather than tap water when dissolving the sodium fluoride.   1

MARKS | DO NOT WRITE IN THIS MARGIN

9. (a) (continued)

(v) The concentration of fluoride ions in a sample of water can be determined by adding the sample to a solution containing a coloured compound. The coloured compound reacts with fluoride ions turning colourless. The higher the concentration of fluoride ions present in a water sample, the paler the colour and the less light is absorbed by the solution.

The graph below shows results for six solutions of known fluoride ion concentration.

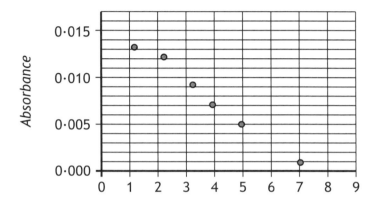

Fluoride ion concentration (mg l^{-1})

Determine the concentration, in mg l^{-1}, of fluoride ions in a water sample that reacted with the coloured compound to form a solution with an absorbance of 0·012.

1

[Turn over

MARKS | DO NOT WRITE IN THIS MARGIN

9. **(continued)**

(b) The concentration of nitrite ions, NO_2^-, in the water supply was determined by titrating water samples with acidified permanganate solutions.

The reaction taking place is

$$2MnO_4^-(aq) \ + \ 5NO_2^-(aq) \ + \ 6H^+(aq) \ \longrightarrow \ 2Mn^{2+}(aq) \ + \ 5NO_3^-(aq) \ + \ 3H_2O(\ell)$$

(i) Name the most appropriate piece of laboratory apparatus to measure out $25 \cdot 0\,cm^3$ samples of water.

1

(ii) $21 \cdot 6\,cm^3$ of $0 \cdot 015\,mol\,l^{-1}$ acidified permanganate solution was required to react completely with the nitrite ions in a $25 \cdot 0\,cm^3$ sample of water.

Calculate the nitrite ion concentration, in $mol\,l^{-1}$, in the water.

Show your working clearly.

3

MARKS | DO NOT WRITE IN THIS MARGIN

10. Soft drinks can contain ingredients such as sweeteners and caffeine.

(a) Aspartame is a sweetener. Its structure is shown below.

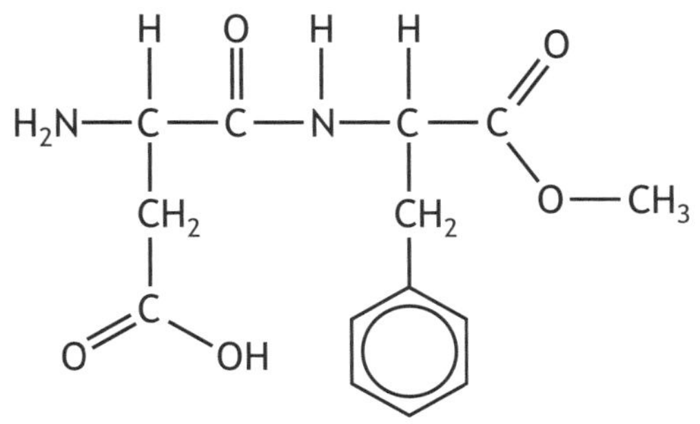

(i) In the stomach, aspartame is hydrolysed by acid to produce two amino acids and an alcohol.

State what is meant by the term 'hydrolysed'.   1

(ii) Name the alcohol produced in the hydrolysis reaction.   1

(iii) The body cannot make all the amino acids it requires and is dependent on protein in the diet for the supply of certain amino acids.

State the term used to describe the amino acids the body cannot make.   1

[Turn over

10. **(continued)**

(b) The concentration of caffeine can be found using chromatography.

A chromatogram for a solution containing $50\,mg\,l^{-1}$ of caffeine is shown below.

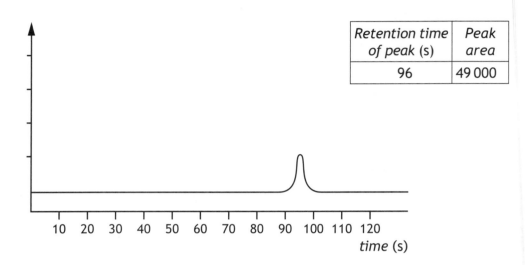

Retention time of peak (s)	Peak area
96	49 000

Results from four caffeine solutions were used to produce the calibration graph below.

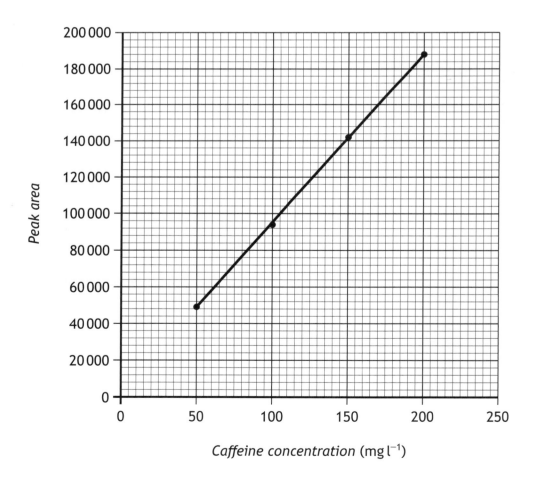

MARKS | DO NOT WRITE IN THIS MARGIN

10. (b) (continued)

(i) The chromatogram for soft drink **X** is shown below.

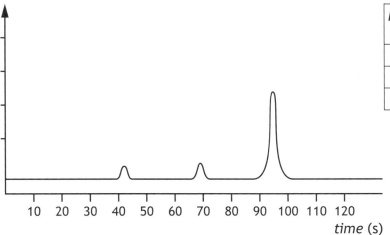

Retention time of peak (s)	Peak area
42	1000
69	1350
96	68 000

Determine the caffeine content, in mg l^{-1}, of soft drink **X**.

1

(ii) The chromatogram for soft drink **Y** is shown below.

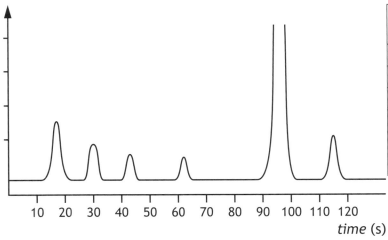

Retention time of peak (s)	Peak area
17	7000
30	4600
43	3000
62	2500
96	- - - -
115	5000

The caffeine content of soft drink **Y** cannot be determined from its chromatogram.

Suggest what could be done to the sample of soft drink **Y** so that the caffeine content could be reliably determined.

1

[Turn over

MARKS | DO NOT WRITE IN THIS MARGIN

11. Hypochlorite bleaches are cleaning products containing the hypochlorite ion, $ClO^-(aq)$, a good oxidising agent.

(a) Hypochlorite bleaches can be made by reacting sodium hydroxide with chlorine. Sodium hypochlorite, NaClO, sodium chloride and water are formed.

Write a balanced equation for the reaction.   **1**

(b) When $ClO^-(aq)$ acts as a bleach, it is reduced to produce the $Cl^-(aq)$ ion.

Complete the ion-electron equation to show the reduction reaction.   **1**

$ClO^-(aq)$ $\rightarrow$ $Cl^-(aq)$

MARKS | DO NOT WRITE IN THIS MARGIN

11. (continued)

(c) In one method that can be used to measure the concentration of hypochlorite ions in a sample of bleach, the bleach sample is reacted with excess hydrogen peroxide.

$$H_2O_2(aq) \ + \ ClO^-(aq) \ \rightarrow \ H_2O(\ell) \ + \ Cl^-(aq) \ + \ O_2(g)$$

By measuring the volume of oxygen given off, the concentration of bleach can be calculated.

(i) Draw a diagram showing an assembled apparatus that could be used to react hydrogen peroxide solution with bleach and measure the volume of oxygen gas released.

Your diagram should include labels showing the names and positions of the reacting chemicals and the collected product.   **3**

(ii) 80 cm^3 of oxygen gas was produced from 5·0 cm^3 of bleach.

Calculate the concentration, in mol l^{-1}, of the hypochlorite ions in the bleach.   **3**

(Take the molar volume of one mole of oxygen to be 24 litres.)

MARKS | DO NOT WRITE IN THIS MARGIN

12. Changing the temperature at which a redox reaction is carried out changes the rate of reaction.

   (a) The effect of temperature on reaction rate can be studied using the rate at which acidified potassium permanganate is reduced by oxalic acid.

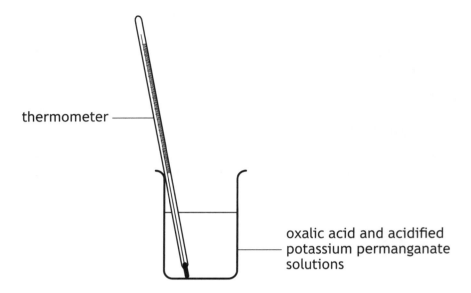

thermometer

oxalic acid and acidified potassium permanganate solutions

   (i) State the colour change that takes place when acidified permanganate ions are reduced.

1

MARKS | DO NOT WRITE IN THIS MARGIN

12.   (a)   (continued)

(ii)   A student's results are shown on the graph below.

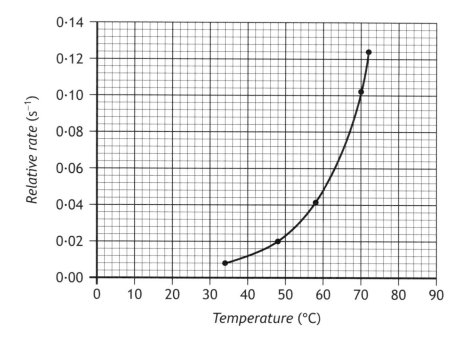

Calculate the time taken for the reaction, in s, when the reaction is carried out at 40 °C.

2

[Turn over

MARKS DO NOT WRITE IN THIS MARGIN

12. **(continued)**

(b)   (i)   Graph 1 shows the distribution of kinetic energy of molecules in a gas at 100 °C.

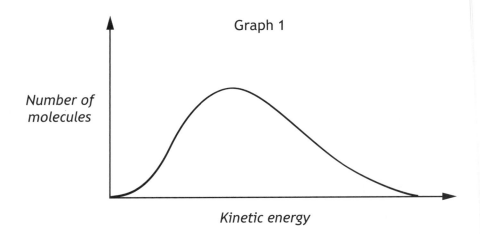

Graph 1

Add a second curve to Graph 1 to show the distribution of kinetic energies at 50 °C.

(An additional graph, if required, can be found on *Page thirty-nine.*)

1

(ii)   In Graph 2, the shaded area represents the number of molecules with the required activation energy, E_a.

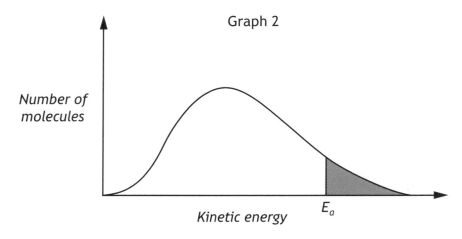

Graph 2

Draw a line to show how a catalyst affects the activation energy.

(An additional graph, if required, can be found on *Page thirty-nine.*)

1

(c)   A collision involving molecules with the required energy of activation may **not** result in a reaction.

State a reason for this.

1

13.   Cis-platin, $PtN_2H_6Cl_2$, is a widely used anti-cancer drug.

It can be produced in the following **exothermic** reaction.

$$K_2PtCl_4(aq) + 2KI(aq) + 2NH_3(g) + 2AgNO_3(aq) \rightleftharpoons PtN_2H_6Cl_2(aq) + 2AgI(s) + 2KNO_3(aq) + 2KCl(aq)$$

The cost of the chemicals used are shown in the table.

Chemical	Cost per gram (£)
K_2PtCl_4	65·00
KI	0·21
NH_3	0·02
$AgNO_3$	3·90

MARKS | DO NOT WRITE IN THIS MARGIN

Using your knowledge of chemistry, comment on how this process could be carried out to make the production of cis-platin as profitable as possible.

3

[END OF SPECIMEN QUESTION PAPER]

ADDITIONAL SPACE FOR ANSWERS AND ROUGH WORK

ADDITIONAL DIAGRAM FOR QUESTION 3 (b)

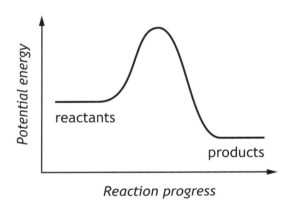

ADDITIONAL DIAGRAM FOR QUESTION 7 (b) (ii)

ADDITIONAL DIAGRAM FOR QUESTION 8 (a)

MARKS | DO NOT WRITE IN THIS MARGIN

ADDITIONAL SPACE FOR ANSWERS AND ROUGH WORK

ADDITIONAL GRAPH FOR QUESTION 12 (b) (i)

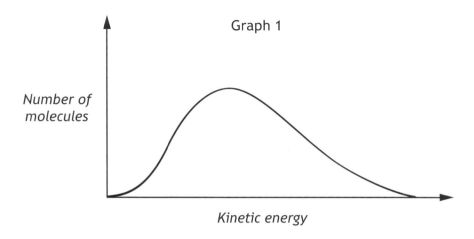

Graph 1

ADDITIONAL GRAPH FOR QUESTION 12 (b) (ii)

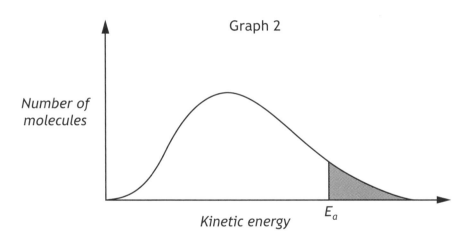

Graph 2

ADDITIONAL SPACE FOR ANSWERS AND ROUGH WORK

MARKS | DO NOT WRITE IN THIS MARGIN

ADDITIONAL SPACE FOR ANSWERS AND ROUGH WORK

[BLANK PAGE]

DO NOT WRITE ON THIS PAGE

National Qualifications 2019

X813/76/12

Chemistry
Paper 1 — Multiple choice

FRIDAY, 10 MAY

9:00 AM – 9:40 AM

Total marks — 25

Attempt ALL questions.

You may use a calculator.

Instructions for the completion of Paper 1 are given on *Page two* of your answer booklet X813/76/02.

Record your answers on the answer grid on *Page three* of your answer booklet.

You may refer to the Chemistry Data Booklet for Higher and Advanced Higher.

Space for rough work is provided at the end of this booklet.

Before leaving the examination room you must give your answer booklet to the Invigilator; if you do not, you may lose all the marks for this paper.

Total marks — 25

Attempt ALL questions

1. Hydrogen will form a non-polar covalent bond with an element that has an electronegativity value of

   A   0·9

   B   1·5

   C   2·2

   D   2·5.

2. Which of the following is a polar molecule?

   A CCl_4

   B NH_3

   C CO_2

   D CH_4

3. Which of the following is most likely to act as a reducing agent?

   A CO

   B MnO_4^-

   C H_2O_2

   D $Cr_2O_7^{2-}$

4. The following reactions take place when nitric acid is added to zinc.

$$NO_3^- (aq) + 4H^+(aq) + 3e^- \rightarrow NO(g) + 2H_2O(\ell)$$

$$Zn(s) \rightarrow Zn^{2+} (aq) + 2e^-$$

   How many moles of $Zn(s)$ are oxidised by one mole of $NO_3^- (aq)$?

   A   0·67

   B   1·0

   C   1·5

   D   2·0

5. Which of the following compounds is a tertiary alcohol?

    A   2,2-dimethylpropan-1-ol

    B   2-methylbutan-2-ol

    C   pentan-3-ol

    D   3-methylbutan-2-ol

6. Molecule **X** has the structure

$$H_2N-\overset{\overset{\displaystyle CH_3}{|}}{CH}-\overset{\overset{\displaystyle O}{\|}}{C}-\overset{\overset{\displaystyle H}{|}}{N}-CH_2-\overset{\overset{\displaystyle O}{\|}}{C}-\overset{\overset{\displaystyle H}{|}}{N}-\overset{\overset{\displaystyle CH(CH_3)_2}{|}}{CH}-COOH$$

    Which of the following could be produced by partial hydrolysis of **X**?

    A $H_2N-CH_2-\overset{\overset{\displaystyle O}{\|}}{C}-\overset{\overset{\displaystyle H}{|}}{N}-\overset{\overset{\displaystyle CH(CH_3)_2}{|}}{CH}-COOH$

    B $H_2N-CH_2-\overset{\overset{\displaystyle O}{\|}}{C}-\overset{\overset{\displaystyle H}{|}}{N}-\overset{\overset{\displaystyle CH_3}{|}}{CH}-COOH$

    C $H_2N-\overset{\overset{\displaystyle CH_3}{|}}{CH}-\overset{\overset{\displaystyle O}{\|}}{C}-\overset{\overset{\displaystyle H}{|}}{N}-\overset{\overset{\displaystyle CH(CH_3)_2}{|}}{CH}-COOH$

    D $H_2N-\overset{\overset{\displaystyle CH(CH_3)_2}{|}}{CH}-\overset{\overset{\displaystyle O}{\|}}{C}-\overset{\overset{\displaystyle H}{|}}{N}-CH_2-COOH$

7. A compound with molecular formula $C_6H_{12}O_2$ could be

    A   pentyl ethanoate

    B   hexan-2-one

    C   3-methylpentan-2-ol

    D   hexanoic acid.

[Turn over

8. Compound X reacted with hot copper(II) oxide and the resulting product did **not** give a colour change when heated with Fehling's solution.

   Compound X could be

   A   pentan-1-ol

   B   pentan-2-ol

   C   pentan-3-one

   D   pentanoic acid.

9. The structure of pivalic acid is shown.

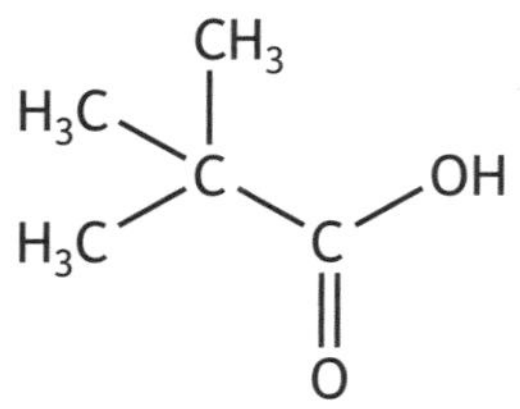

   Which of the following is the correct systematic name of pivalic acid?

   A   pentanoic acid

   B   2,2,2-trimethylethanoic acid

   C   2-ethylpropanoic acid

   D   2,2-dimethylpropanoic acid

10. The table shows four compounds that contribute to the aroma of spices.

    Which compound is **not** derived from a terpene?

	Structural formula	Molecular formula
A		$C_{10}H_{14}O$
B		$C_{10}H_{12}O$
C		$C_{10}H_{18}O$
D		C_9H_8O

11. Which reaction can be classified as reduction?

    A   methanol $\rightarrow$ methanoic acid

    B   propanal $\rightarrow$ propanoic acid

    C   butan-2-one $\rightarrow$ butan-2-ol

    D   propan-2-ol $\rightarrow$ propanone

[Turn over

12. A secondary amine has two carbon atoms directly bonded to the nitrogen atom. Which of the following is a secondary amine?

A

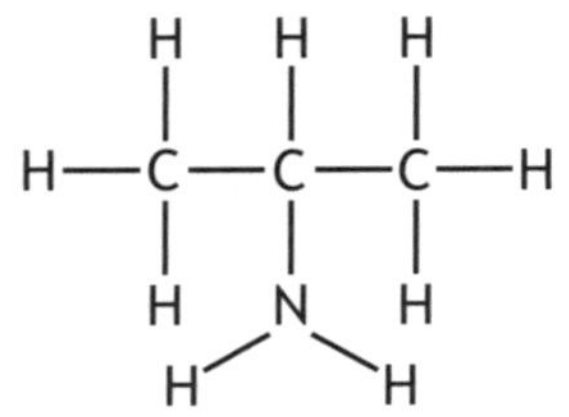

B

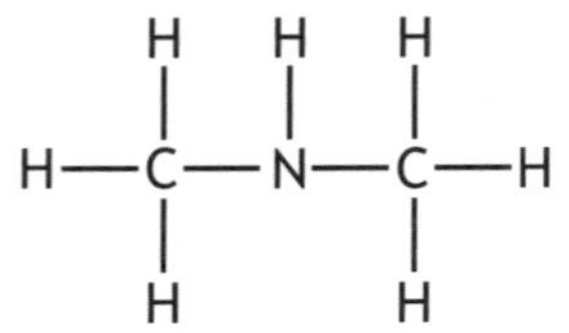

C

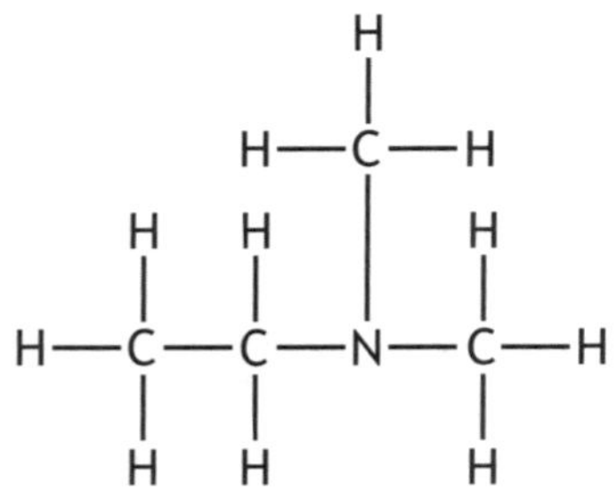

D

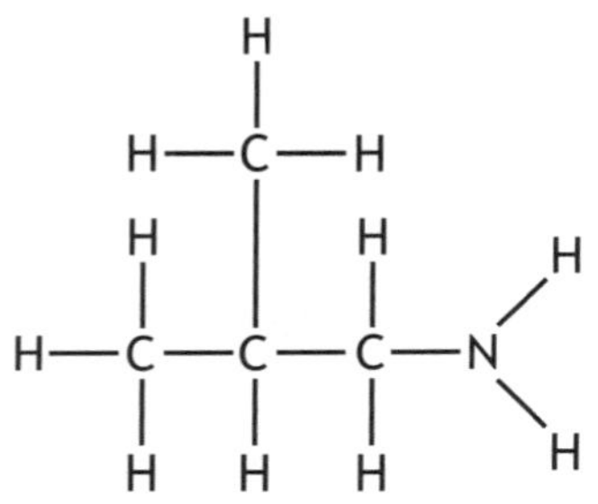

13. The number of moles of ions in 1 mol of copper(II) phosphate is

A   1

B   2

C   3

D   5.

14. Which of the following gas samples has the same volume as 4·0 g of methane, CH_4?
(All volumes are measured at the same temperature and pressure.)

A   1·0 g of helium

B   1·0 g of hydrogen

C   3·5 g of nitrogen

D   35·5 g of chlorine

15. Magnesium carbonate reacts with nitric acid.

$$MgCO_3(s) + 2HNO_3(aq) \rightarrow Mg(NO_3)_2(aq) + H_2O(\ell) + CO_2(g)$$

0·05 mol of magnesium carbonate was added to a solution containing 0·06 mol of nitric acid.
Which of the following statements is true?

A   0·05 mol of carbon dioxide is produced

B   0·06 mol of magnesium nitrate is produced

C   Magnesium carbonate is in excess by 0·02 mol

D   Nitric acid is in excess by 0·01 mol

[Turn over

16. In which of the following diagrams does the dotted line represent a permanent dipole-permanent dipole interaction between propanone molecules?

A

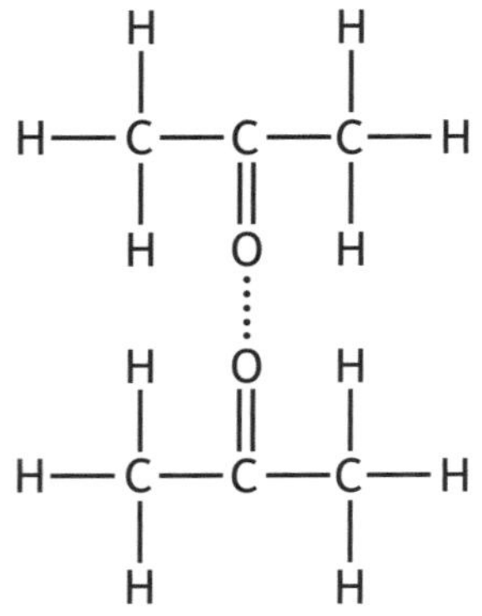

B

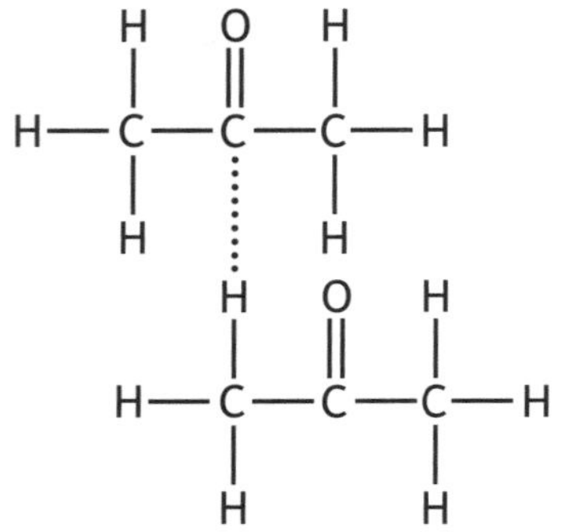

C

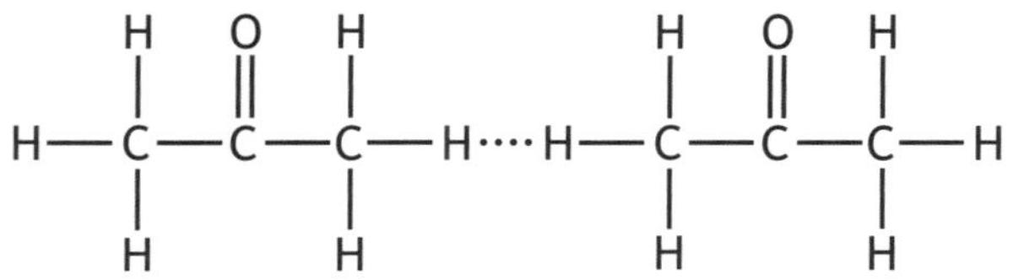

D

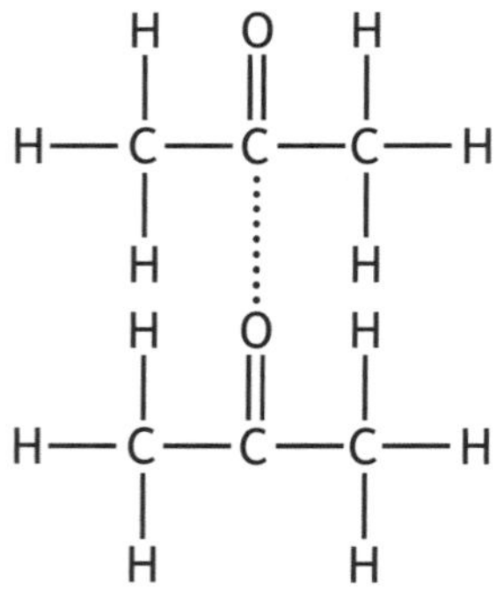

17. Iron can be produced from iron(III) oxide.

$$2Fe_2O_3(s) \quad + \quad 3C(s) \quad \rightarrow \quad 4Fe(s) \quad + \quad 3CO_2(g)$$

GFM = 159·6 g   GFM = 12·0 g   GFM = 55·8 g   GFM = 44·0 g

The atom economy for the production of iron is

A   69·9%

B   62·8%

C   58·2%

D   32·5%.

18. $100\,cm^3$ of propane is mixed with $600\,cm^3$ of oxygen and the mixture is ignited.

$$C_3H_8(g) \quad + \quad 5O_2(g) \quad \rightarrow \quad 3CO_2(g) \quad + \quad 4H_2O(\ell)$$

At the end of the reaction, the total volume of gas would be

A $300\,cm^3$

B $400\,cm^3$

C $700\,cm^3$

D $800\,cm^3$.

19. A two-step reaction is shown below.

A $\xrightarrow{\text{step 1}}$ B $\xrightarrow{\text{step 2}}$ C

The first step gave a yield of 60% and the second step a yield of 90%.
The overall yield would be

A   30%

B   54%

C   67%

D   150%.

[Turn over

20. The volume of hydrogen gas given off against time when an excess of zinc lumps is added to 100 cm³ of 1 mol l⁻¹ hydrochloric acid is shown.

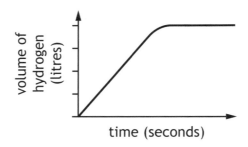

Which of the following graphs would show the volume of hydrogen gas given off when an excess of zinc powder was added to 50 cm³ of 1 mol l⁻¹ hydrochloric acid?

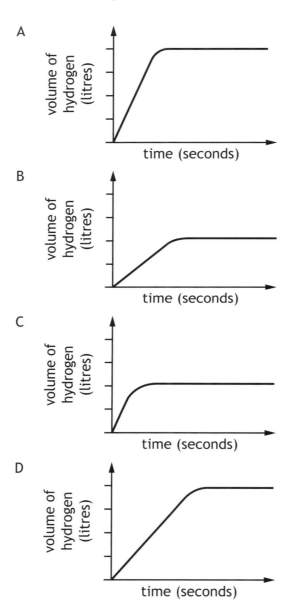

21. Consider the reaction pathway shown below.

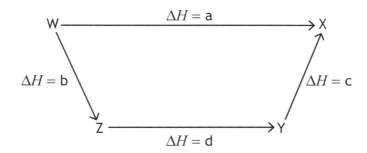

According to Hess's Law

A $b = a - c - d$

B $b = a + c + d$

C $b = d - c + a$

D $b = d + c - a$.

22. Which of the following is **not** a factor that affects the rate of a reaction?

A   Activation energy

B   Kinetic energies of reactant molecules

C   Concentration of reactants

D   Enthalpy change of reaction

23. In which of the following reactions would the yield of product be increased by lowering the pressure?

A $H_2(g) + I_2(g) \rightleftharpoons 2HI(g)$

B $N_2(g) + 3H_2(g) \rightleftharpoons 2NH_3(g)$

C $N_2O_4(g) \rightleftharpoons 2NO_2(g)$

D $CO(g) + 2H_2(g) \rightleftharpoons CH_3OH(g)$

[Turn over

24. The graph shows the distribution of kinetic energies for a reaction involving two gases.

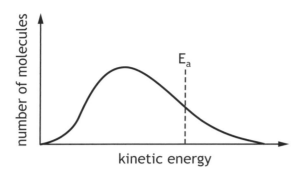

Which graph would show the effect of increasing temperature?

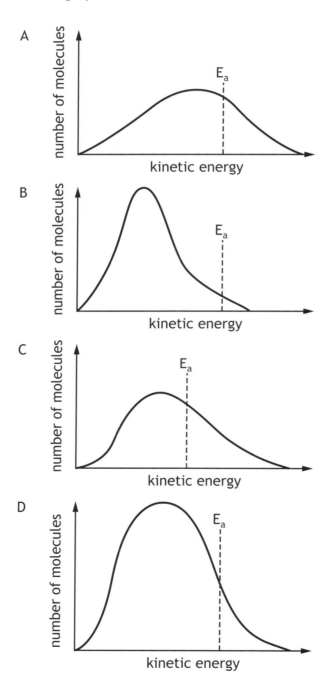

25. Alkenes react with ozone, O_3, to form ozonides which can be decomposed to give carbonyl compounds.

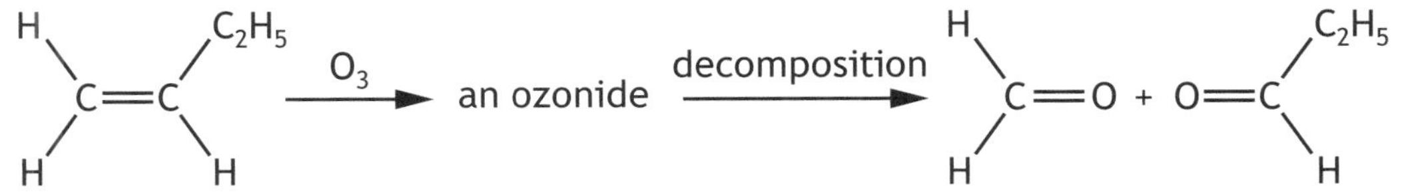

Which of the following alkenes would produce a mixture of ethanal and propanone?

A $CH_3CH=CHCH_2CH_3$

B $CH_3CH=CHCH_3$

C $CH_3C=CH_2$
    |
    CH_3

D $CH_3CH=CCH_3$
    |
    CH_3

[END OF QUESTION PAPER]

SPACE FOR ROUGH WORK

SPACE FOR ROUGH WORK

[BLANK PAGE]

DO NOT WRITE ON THIS PAGE

FOR OFFICIAL USE

National Qualifications 2019

Mark

X813/76/02

Chemistry
Paper 1 — Multiple choice
Answer booklet

FRIDAY, 10 MAY
9:00 AM – 9:40 AM

Fill in these boxes and read what is printed below.

Full name of centre

Town

Forename(s)

Surname

Number of seat

Date of birth
Day   Month   Year   Scottish candidate number

Instructions for the completion of Paper 1 are given on *Page two*.

Record your answers on the answer grid on *Page three*.

Use **blue** or **black** ink.

Before leaving the examination room you must give your answer booklet to the Invigilator; if you do not, you may lose all the marks for this paper.

Paper 1 — 25 marks

The questions for Paper 1 are contained in the question paper X813/76/12.

Read these and record your answers on the answer grid on *Page three*.

Use **blue** or **black** ink. Do NOT use gel pens or pencil.

1. The answer to each question is **either** A, B, C or D. Decide what your answer is, then fill in the appropriate bubble (see sample question below).

2. There is **only one correct** answer to each question.

3. Any rough working should be done on the space for rough work at the end of the question paper X813/76/12.

Sample question

To show that the ink in a ball-pen consists of a mixture of dyes, the method of separation would be:

    A   fractional distillation

    B   chromatography

    C   fractional crystallisation

    D   filtration.

The correct answer is **B** — chromatography. The answer **B** bubble has been clearly filled in (see below).

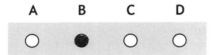

Changing an answer

If you decide to change your answer, cancel your first answer by putting a cross through it (see below) and fill in the answer you want. The answer below has been changed to **D**.

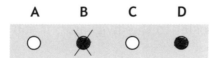

If you then decide to change back to an answer you have already scored out, put a tick (✔) to the **right** of the answer you want, as shown below:

Paper 1 — Answer Grid

	A	B	C	D
1	○	○	○	○
2	○	○	○	○
3	○	○	○	○
4	○	○	○	○
5	○	○	○	○
6	○	○	○	○
7	○	○	○	○
8	○	○	○	○
9	○	○	○	○
10	○	○	○	○
11	○	○	○	○
12	○	○	○	○
13	○	○	○	○
14	○	○	○	○
15	○	○	○	○
16	○	○	○	○
17	○	○	○	○
18	○	○	○	○
19	○	○	○	○
20	○	○	○	○
21	○	○	○	○
22	○	○	○	○
23	○	○	○	○
24	○	○	○	○
25	○	○	○	○

[BLANK PAGE]

DO NOT WRITE ON THIS PAGE

H

National Qualifications 2019

Mark

X813/76/01

Chemistry
Paper 2

FRIDAY, 10 MAY

10:10 AM – 12:30 PM

Fill in these boxes and read what is printed below.

Full name of centre

Town

Forename(s)

Surname

Number of seat

Date of birth

Day	Month	Year	Scottish candidate number

Total marks — 95

Attempt ALL questions.

You may use a calculator.

You may refer to the Chemistry Data Booklet for Higher and Advanced Higher.

Write your answers clearly in the spaces provided in this booklet. Additional space for answers and rough work is provided at the end of this booklet. If you use this space you must clearly identify the question number you are attempting. Any rough work must be written in this booklet. Score through your rough work when you have written your final copy.

Use **blue** or **black** ink.

Before leaving the examination room you must give this booklet to the Invigilator; if you do not, you may lose all the marks for this paper.

MARKS | DO NOT WRITE IN THIS MARGIN

Total marks — 95

Attempt ALL questions

1. Sodium thiosulfate, $Na_2S_2O_3$, can be used to investigate the effect of reaction conditions on the rate of reaction.

    (a) Sodium thiosulfate solution reacts with hydrochloric acid to form a precipitate of solid sulfur. By placing the reaction mixture in a conical flask over a cross and recording the time taken for the cross to disappear, the effect of changing the reaction conditions can be investigated.

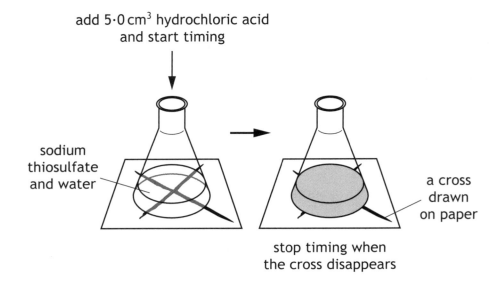

add $5{\cdot}0\,cm^3$ hydrochloric acid and start timing

sodium thiosulfate and water

a cross drawn on paper

stop timing when the cross disappears

    (i) The equation for the reaction is

$$Na_2S_2O_3(aq) + HCl(aq) \rightarrow S(s) + SO_2(g) + NaCl(aq) + H_2O(\ell)$$

Balance the equation.   **1**

MARKS | DO NOT WRITE IN THIS MARGIN

1. (a) (continued)

(ii) In one set of experiments, the effect of varying the concentration of sodium thiosulfate was investigated.

Experiment	Volume of $0.15 \, mol \, l^{-1}$ $Na_2S_2O_3$ (cm^3)	Volume of water (cm^3)	Rate (s^{-1})
A	50	0	0·0454
B	40		0·0370
C	30		0·0285
D	20		0·0169
E	10	40	0·0063

(A) Complete the table to show the volumes of water that would have been used to vary the concentration of sodium thiosulfate.   **1**

(B) Calculate the time, in seconds, for the cross to disappear in experiment C.   **1**

[Turn over

1. (a) (continued)

(iii) The reaction can also be used to investigate the effect of changing temperature on the rate of reaction.

The results from an investigation are shown in the graph below.

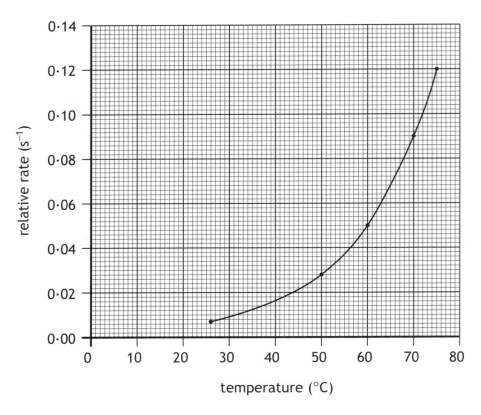

Use the graph to determine the temperature rise, in °C, required to double the rate of the reaction.

1

(b) Collision theory states that for particles to react they must first collide with each other.

State **two** conditions necessary for the collisions to result in the formation of products.

2

MARKS | DO NOT WRITE IN THIS MARGIN

1. **(continued)**

(c) Sodium thiosulfate also reacts with iron(III) nitrate.

The potential energy diagram below shows the change in potential energy during the reaction carried out without a catalyst.

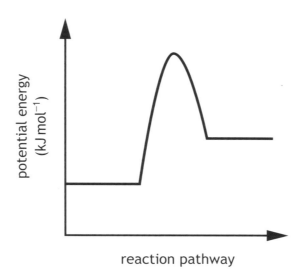

reaction pathway

(i) Draw an **X** on the potential energy diagram above to show where the activated complex is formed.

(An additional diagram, if required, can be found on *Page forty-one*).

1

(ii) Cu^{2+} ions catalyse the reaction.

Add a dotted line to the diagram to show the change in potential energy with the catalyst.

(An additional diagram, if required, can be found on *Page forty-one*).

1

[Turn over

MARKS | DO NOT WRITE IN THIS MARGIN

2. 2019 is the 150th anniversary of the periodic table's creation by Dmitri Mendeleev. The patterns identified by Mendeleev form the basis of the modern periodic table. The major periodic trends include ionisation energy and covalent radius.

    (a) The first ionisation energies of elements with atomic number 1 to 20 are shown in the graph.

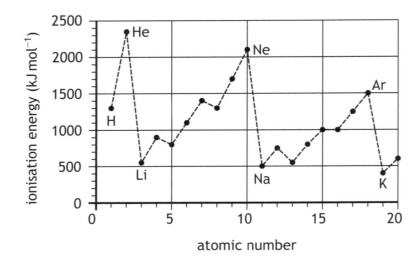

    (i) Explain why the first ionisation energy shows an increase going from lithium to neon.

    1

    (ii) Explain why the first ionisation energy of potassium is less than the first ionisation energy of lithium.

    1

MARKS | DO NOT WRITE IN THIS MARGIN

2. (continued)

(b) A graph showing the ionisation energies for nitrogen is shown.

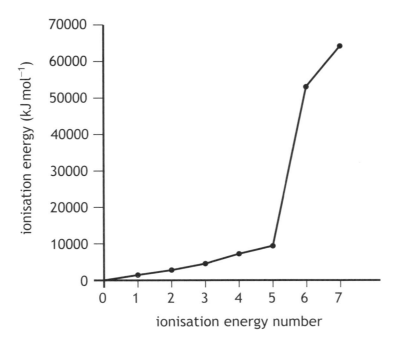

(i) Write the equation for the second ionisation energy of nitrogen.   **1**

(ii) Explain **fully** the increase between the 5th and 6th ionisation energies of nitrogen.   **2**

[Turn over

MARKS | DO NOT WRITE IN THIS MARGIN

2. **(continued)**

(c) Ionic radius is a measure of the size of an ion.

Explain **fully** why the ionic radius of phosphorus is greater than the ionic radius of aluminium.

2

2.   **(continued)**

(d)   The structure of an ionic compound consists of a giant lattice of oppositely charged ions. The arrangement of ions is determined by the 'radius ratio' of the ions involved.

$$\text{radius ratio} = \frac{\text{radius of positive ion}}{\text{radius of negative ion}}$$

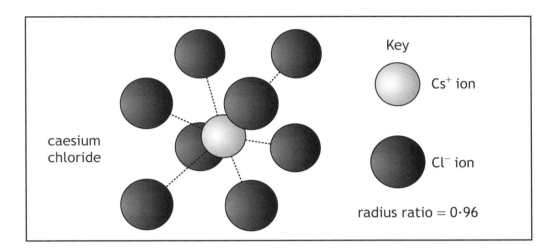

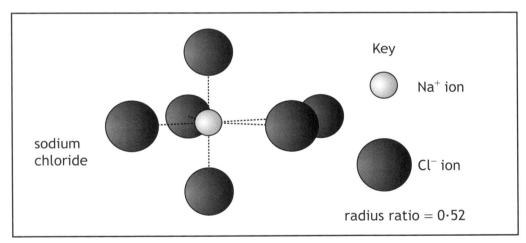

By using the table of ionic radii on *Page seventeen* of the data booklet, predict whether the structure of barium oxide, BaO, is similar to caesium chloride or sodium chloride.

Your answer **must** include a calculated radius ratio.

1

3. The melting point of **non-metal elements** depends on structure and bonding.

    Using your knowledge of chemistry, comment on this statement.   3

MARKS | DO NOT WRITE IN THIS MARGIN

4. Cider is made from apples in a process that involves crushing and pressing the apples, converting the sugars into alcohol, maturing and bottling.

(a) Brewers add yeast, which contains a mixture of enzymes to convert the sugars in the apples into alcohol and carbon dioxide.

   (i) State what is meant by the term enzyme. **1**

   (ii) The % mass of alcohol in the cider can be calculated using the formula

   $$\% \text{ mass of alcohol} = \frac{\text{mass of alcohol}}{\text{mass of cider}} \times 100$$

   A $50 \cdot 0 \, cm^3$ sample of cider was found to contain $3 \cdot 05 \, g$ of alcohol. $1 \cdot 0 \, cm^3$ of the cider weighed $1 \cdot 36 \, g$.

   Calculate the % mass of alcohol in the cider. **1**

(b) During the maturing process malic acid is converted to lactic acid and another product.

malic acid   lactic acid

   (i) Name compound X. **1**

[Turn over

4. (b) (continued)

(ii) The maturing process in cider samples can be monitored using thin layer chromatography.

Samples of lactic acid, malic acid and ciders A, B, C, and D are spotted on a silica plate and the solvent allowed to travel up the plate. The chromatogram obtained is shown below.

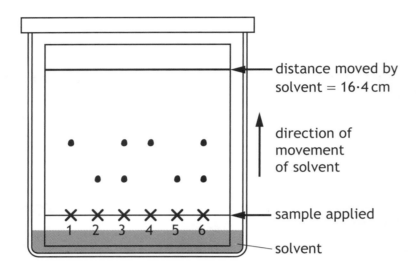

distance moved by solvent = 16·4 cm

direction of movement of solvent

sample applied

solvent

Number	Sample applied	Distance moved by spot(s) (cm)
1	lactic acid	8·2
2	malic acid	4·1
3	cider A	4·1, 8·2
4	cider B	8·2
5	cider C	4·1
6	cider D	4·1, 8·2

MARKS | DO NOT WRITE IN THIS MARGIN

4. (b) (ii) **(continued)**

The retention factor, R_f, for a substance can be a useful method of identifying the substance.

$$R_f = \frac{\text{distance moved by the substance}}{\text{distance moved by the solvent}}$$

(A) Calculate the R_f value of malic acid.

1

(B) The maturing process is complete when all of the malic acid has been converted to lactic acid. The cider is now ready to be bottled.

Use the chromatogram to determine which cider is ready to be bottled.

1

[Turn over

MARKS | DO NOT WRITE IN THIS MARGIN

4. **(continued)**

(c) Glycerol can be added to cider before bottling to produce a sweeter tasting cider.

State the systematic name for glycerol.   **1**

(d) Cider contains many naturally occurring compounds that affect taste and aroma.

(i) Procyanidin B2 provides a bitter taste to cider.

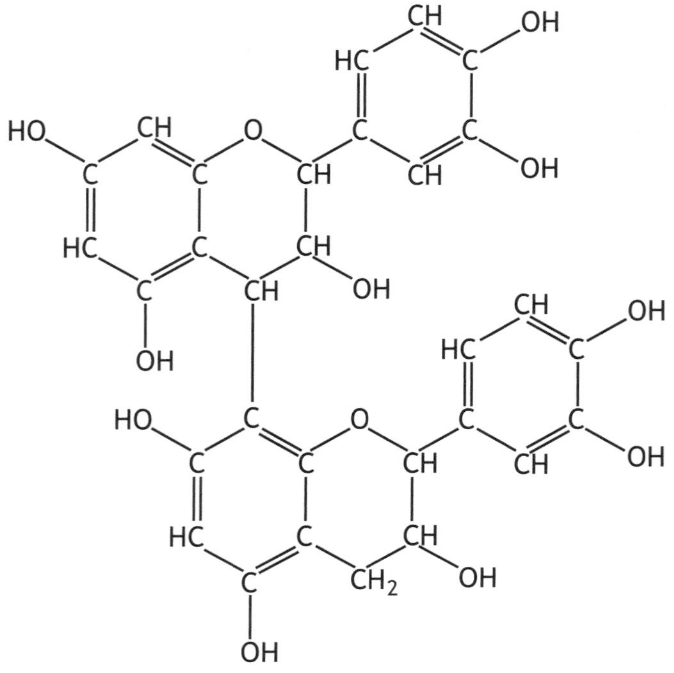

procyanidin B2

Explain **fully** why procyanidin B2 is water soluble.   **2**

MARKS | DO NOT WRITE IN THIS MARGIN

4. (d) (continued)

(ii) Cider smells of apples because it contains ethyl 2-methylbutanoate.

ethyl 2-methylbutanoate

Name the carboxylic acid used to make ethyl 2-methylbutanoate.   **1**

(iii) Farnesene is a terpene responsible for the ripe apple aroma of cider.

farnesene

Name the molecule on which terpenes are based.   **1**

(e) Ethanol in cider can be oxidised to ethanal, spoiling the aroma.

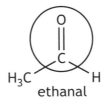

ethanal

(i) Name the functional group circled in the ethanal molecule.   **1**

(ii) Further oxidation of ethanal can produce another product that spoils the flavour of cider.

Name this product.   **1**

MARKS | DO NOT WRITE IN THIS MARGIN

5. The combustion reactions of methane and heptane can be studied in different ways.

(a) The combustion of methane produces carbon dioxide and water vapour when carried out at temperatures above $100\,^\circ C$.

$$CH_4(g) \quad + \quad 2O_2(g) \quad \rightarrow \quad CO_2(g) \quad + \quad 2H_2O(g)$$

(i) Using bond enthalpies and mean bond enthalpies from the data booklet, calculate the enthalpy change, in $kJ\,mol^{-1}$, for this reaction.

2

(ii) Explain the difference between bond enthalpy and mean bond enthalpy.

1

MARKS | DO NOT WRITE IN THIS MARGIN

5. (a) (continued)

(iii) Calculate the mass, in g, of carbon dioxide produced by combustion of $200\,cm^3$ methane in excess oxygen.

2

Take the volume of 1 mole of methane gas to be 24 litres.

$$CH_4(g) \quad + \quad 2O_2(g) \quad \rightarrow \quad CO_2(g) \quad + \quad 2H_2O(g)$$

$$GFM = 44{\cdot}0\,g$$

[Turn over

MARKS | DO NOT WRITE IN THIS MARGIN

5. **(continued)**

(b) The enthalpy of combustion of heptane, C_7H_{16}, can be determined using a calorimeter.

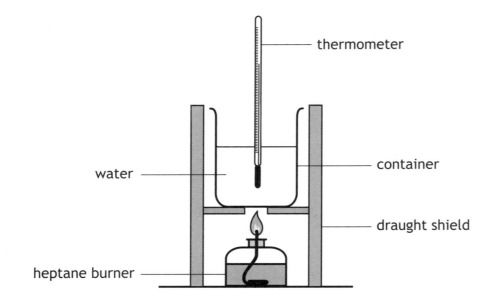

The following results were obtained.

Mass of heptane burned (g)	1·1
Mass of 1 mole of heptane (g)	100·0
Volume of water used (cm^3)	400
Initial temperature of water (°C)	26
Final temperature of water (°C)	49

(i) State the measurements required to calculate the mass of heptane burned in this experiment. **1**

MARKS | DO NOT WRITE IN THIS MARGIN

5.   (b)   (continued)

(ii)   Calculate the enthalpy of combustion, in $kJ\,mol^{-1}$, for heptane from the experimental results given.   **3**

(iii)   The theoretical value for the enthalpy of combustion of heptane is significantly higher than the experimental value.

Suggest why the experimental value is different to the theoretical value.   **1**

[Turn over

MARKS | DO NOT WRITE IN THIS MARGIN

6. Thiols are compounds that contain an —SH functional group. They often have very strong, unpleasant odours.

(a) Ethanethiol is used to add a smell to gaseous fuels in order to give warnings of gas leaks.

ethanethiol

(i) A student used the boiling points of ethanethiol and propan-1-ol to compare the strength of intermolecular forces.

ethanethiol
boiling point = 35 °C

propan-1-ol
boiling point = 97 °C

(A) State the reason why propan-1-ol was a suitable alcohol to compare with ethanethiol. **1**

(B) Explain why propan-1-ol has a higher boiling point than ethanethiol. Your answer should include the names of the intermolecular forces broken when each liquid boils. **2**

MARKS | DO NOT WRITE IN THIS MARGIN

6. **(a)** **(continued)**

(ii) Name the thiol that contains only one carbon atom. **1**

(iii) The minimum concentration of ethanethiol in air that can be detected by humans is $2 \cdot 7 \times 10^{-7}$ mg per cm^3 of air.

Calculate the minimum mass of ethanethiol that needs to be present in a room containing 43 900 litres of air in order for it to be detected. **2**

(b) 2-methyl-2-propanethiol is also used to add a smell to gaseous fuels.

```
        H    SH   H
        |    |    |
  H —— C —— C —— C —— H
        |    |    |
        H   CH₃   H
```

2-methyl-2-propanethiol

(i) Suggest why 2-methyl-2-propanethiol is classified as a tertiary thiol. **1**

[Turn over

MARKS | DO NOT WRITE IN THIS MARGIN

6. (b) (continued)

(ii) Thiols can be made by the addition of hydrogen sulfide to alkenes.

2-methyl-2-propanethiol can be made by the addition reaction shown.

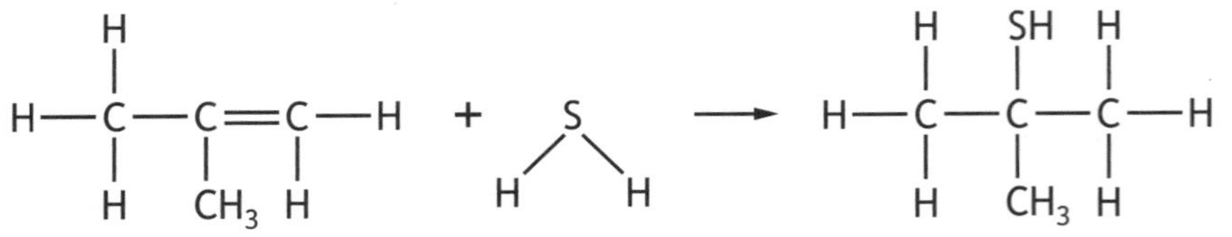

2-methylpropene
GFM = 56·0 g

2-methyl-2-propanethiol
GFM = 90·1 g

(A) Draw the structure for the other isomer formed in this addition reaction.

1

(B) A chemist obtained an 84% yield of 2-methyl-2-propanethiol after starting with 30·5 g of 2-methylpropene.

Calculate the mass, in g, of 2-methyl-2-propanethiol made by the chemist.

2

7. Esters can be synthetic or natural.

(a) The synthetic polyester PET, poly(ethylene terephthalate), has many ester links. PET can break down by a free radical reaction.

One of the steps involved in breaking down PET is shown.

(i) State the name for this step. **1**

(ii) Name the component of sunlight that can cause plastics such as PET to break down. **1**

(iii) Name the type of substance that can be added to plastics to prevent them breaking down in this way. **1**

[Turn over

MARKS | DO NOT WRITE IN THIS MARGIN

7. (continued)

(b)   (i) Natural cyclic esters called lactones can be formed from hydroxycarboxylic acids.

5-hydroxypentanoic acid is a hydroxycarboxylic acid that when heated, with dilute acid, will form a cyclic ester.

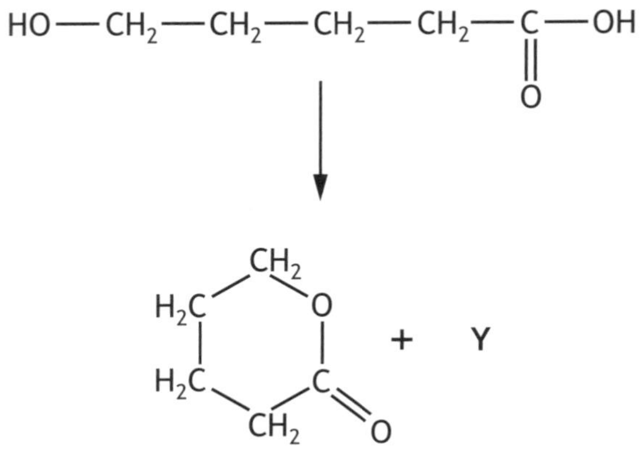

Name product **Y** in this reaction.   **1**

(ii) Draw the structure for the cyclic compound formed when 4-hydroxypentanoic acid is heated with dilute acid.   **1**

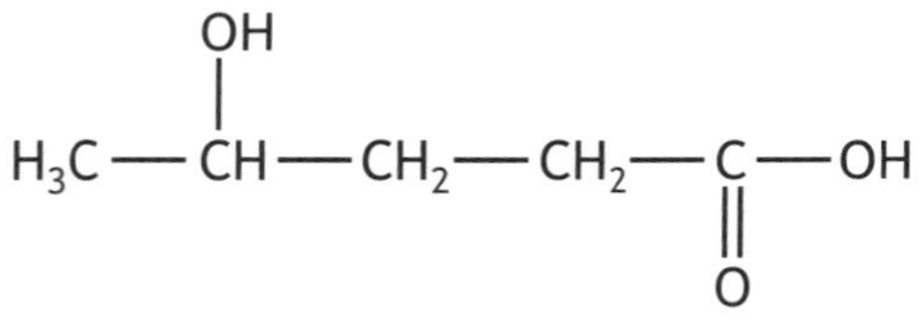

4-hydroxypentanoic acid

MARKS | DO NOT WRITE IN THIS MARGIN

7. (b) (continued)

(iii) Name the hydroxycarboxylic acid shown below. **1**

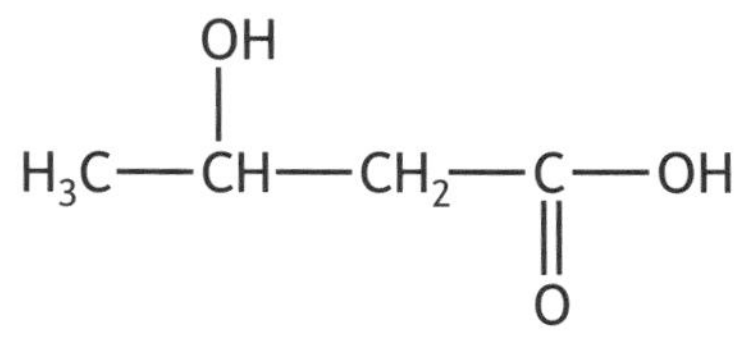

$$H_3C-\underset{\underset{OH}{|}}{CH}-CH_2-\underset{\underset{O}{\|}}{C}-OH$$

[Turn over

8. Gelatin is a soluble protein that can be added to different food products.

(a) A structure for a section of a protein chain in gelatin is shown.

(i) State the number of amino acids that joined together to form the section of the protein chain shown.

1

(ii) Name the weakest van der Waals' force between water and gelatin molecules.

1

(b) A student was investigating the viscosity of different concentrations of gelatin solution.

(i) The student was asked to prepare a 2% gelatin solution, which is a solution that contains 2 g of gelatin per $100\,cm^3$ of solution.

The student prepared this solution by adding $100\,cm^3$ of distilled water into a volumetric flask, then adding 2 g of gelatin.

Describe how the student **should** have made up the solution.

3

MARKS | DO NOT WRITE IN THIS MARGIN

8. (b) (continued)

(ii) The results obtained from the student's viscosity experiment are shown.

Concentration of gelatin solution (%)	Viscosity (units)
2·0	1·0
4·0	2·0
6·0	4·0
8·0	7·0
10·0	

Predict the student's result for the viscosity, in units, of a 10·0% gelatin solution.

1

(c) Bromelain is a mixture of enzymes found in pineapple that aid digestion.

(i) Adding raw pineapple to gelatin results in the gelatin molecules being hydrolysed. The rate of hydrolysis is reduced if the pineapple is cooked.

Explain why the rate of hydrolysis is reduced.

1

(ii) Bromelain can be purchased as tablets that contain 500 mg of bromelain. The flesh from a pineapple contains 13·2 mg of bromelain per gram.

Calculate the mass, in g, of this pineapple that would be needed to provide 500 mg of bromelain.

1

[Turn over

9. Chlorine is used in the production of many other chemicals.

   (a) Chlorine can be produced by the reaction of hydrogen chloride with air using the Deacon process.

   $$4HCl(g) + O_2(g) \rightleftharpoons 2Cl_2(g) + 2H_2O(g)$$

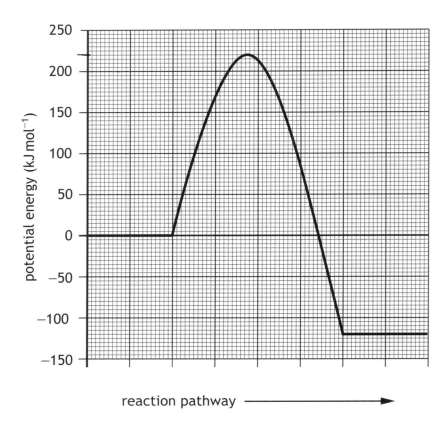

reaction pathway ⟶

   (i) Using the potential energy diagram, determine the activation energy, in $kJ\,mol^{-1}$, for the **forward** reaction.

   1

   (ii) Explain why increasing the temperature in the Deacon process results in less chlorine being produced.

   1

MARKS | DO NOT WRITE IN THIS MARGIN

9.   (continued)

(b)   One laboratory method for the preparation of chlorine gas involves adding concentrated hydrochloric acid to potassium permanganate. The chlorine gas produced also contains small amounts of hydrogen chloride gas. To remove the hydrogen chloride gas the gases are bubbled through water. Finally, insoluble chlorine gas is collected.

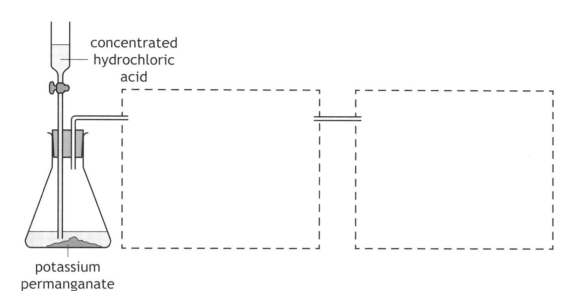

Complete a labelled diagram to show an apparatus suitable for carrying out this preparation.

(An additional diagram, if required, can be found on *Page forty-one*)

2

[**Turn over**

9. **(continued)**

(c) Carbon tetrachloride, CCl_4, is prepared by the reaction of chlorine gas, Cl_2, with methane, CH_4.

$$CH_4(g) + 4Cl_2(g) \rightarrow CCl_4(g) + 4HCl(g)$$

Calculate the enthalpy change, in $kJ\,mol^{-1}$, for this reaction using the following information.

2

$C(s) + 2H_2(g)$	$\rightarrow$	$CH_4(g)$	$\Delta H = -75\,kJ\,mol^{-1}$	rev
$C(s) + 2Cl_2(g)$	$\rightarrow$	$CCl_4(g)$	$\Delta H = -98\,kJ\,mol^{-1}$	
$\frac{1}{2}H_2(g) + \frac{1}{2}Cl_2(g)$	$\rightarrow$	$HCl(g)$	$\Delta H = -92\,kJ\,mol^{-1}$	$\times 4$

[Turn over for next question

DO NOT WRITE ON THIS PAGE

MARKS | DO NOT WRITE IN THIS MARGIN

10. A student investigated the purity of a sample of magnesium chloride, $MgCl_2$. The sample was dissolved in water and then an excess of silver nitrate, $AgNO_3$, was added to produce a precipitate of silver chloride, $AgCl$. The precipitate was collected, dried and weighed.

$$MgCl_2(aq) + 2AgNO_3(aq) \rightarrow 2AgCl(s) + Mg(NO_3)_2(aq)$$

(a) The student prepared the magnesium chloride solution by dissolving 2·503 g of impure magnesium chloride in water.

Explain why the student should use distilled or deionised water, rather than tap water, when preparing the solution.

1

(b) (i) Complete the table to show the **most appropriate** piece of apparatus that could be used to measure the required volumes.

2

Measurement	Apparatus
20·0 cm³ **(accurately)**	
35 cm³ **(approximately)**	

(ii) The steps required to collect, dry and weigh the precipitate are listed below. However, the steps are in the **wrong order**.

A. Weigh the precipitate and the filter paper

B. Wash the precipitate with water to remove any impurities

C. Filter the precipitate

D. Dry the precipitate in an oven

E. Weigh the filter paper

Complete the flow chart below to show the correct order of steps the student should carry out to collect, dry and weigh the precipitate.

1

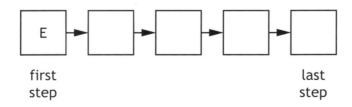

first step ... last step

(An additional diagram, if required, can be found on *Page forty-one*)

MARKS | DO NOT WRITE IN THIS MARGIN

10. **(b)** **(continued)**

(iii) $1 \cdot 393$ g of silver chloride precipitate was produced from the magnesium chloride solution.

$$MgCl_2(aq) \quad + \quad 2AgNO_3(aq) \quad \rightarrow \quad 2AgCl(s) \quad + \quad Mg(NO_3)_2(aq)$$

$$GFM = 95 \cdot 3\,g \qquad\qquad\qquad GFM = 143 \cdot 4\,g$$

Calculate the mass of magnesium chloride, in g, present in the magnesium chloride solution.

2

(c) The average mass of magnesium chloride in $2 \cdot 503$ g of the original impure sample was calculated to be $2 \cdot 403$ g.

Calculate the % of magnesium chloride present in the original sample.

1

[Turn over

11. Differences in physical and chemical properties can be used to distinguish one compound from another.

The compounds extracted from orange juice include antioxidants, flavour molecules, essential oils, aroma molecules and coloured molecules.

Some examples of these are shown below.

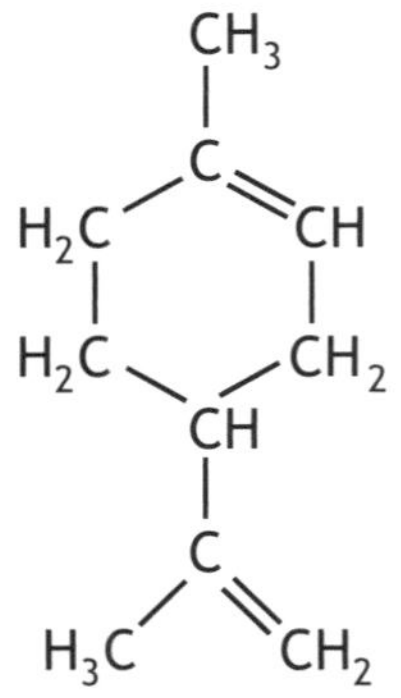

limonene

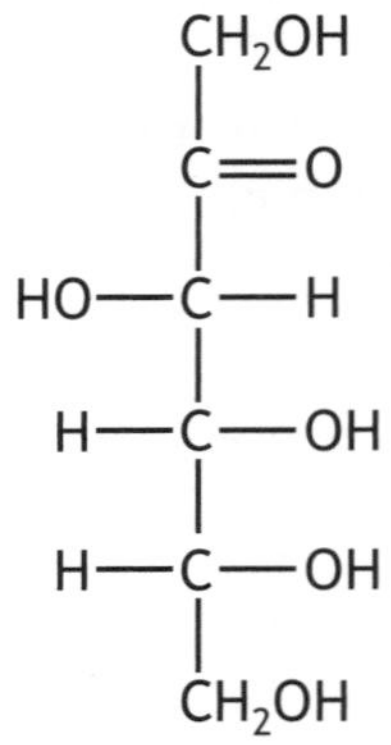

fructose

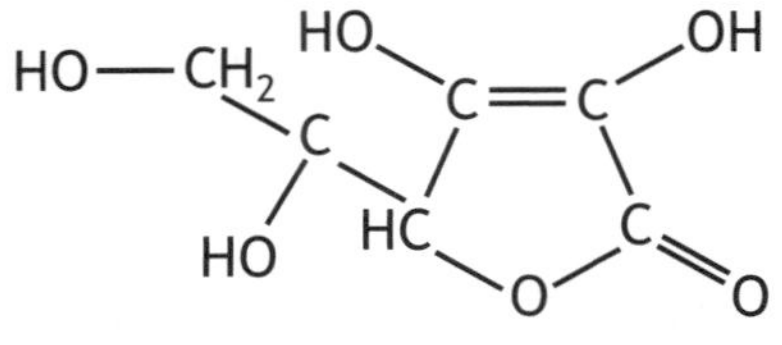

vitamin C

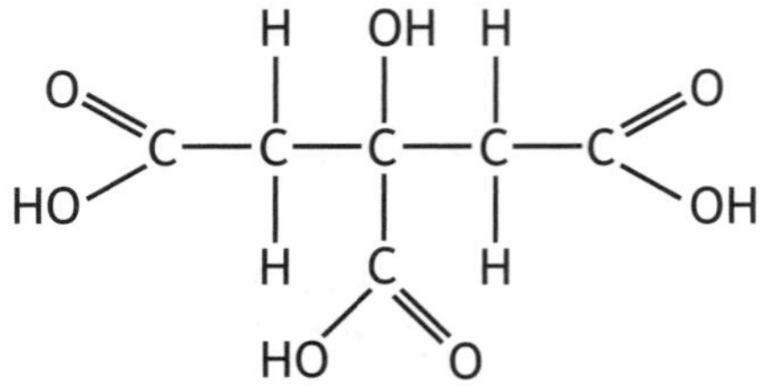

citric acid

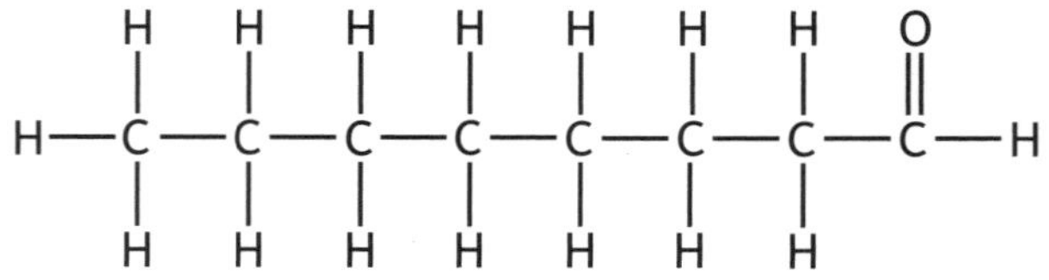

octanal

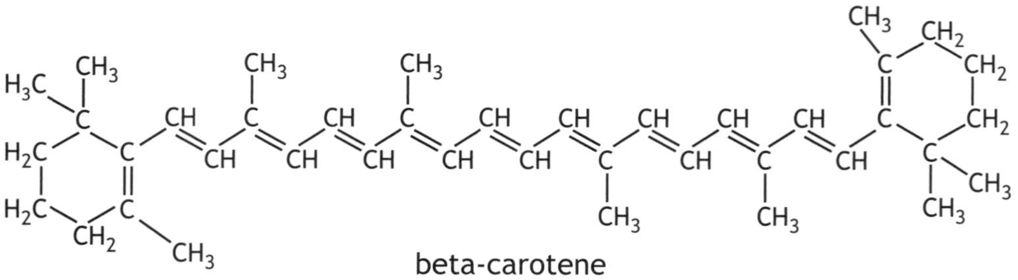

beta-carotene

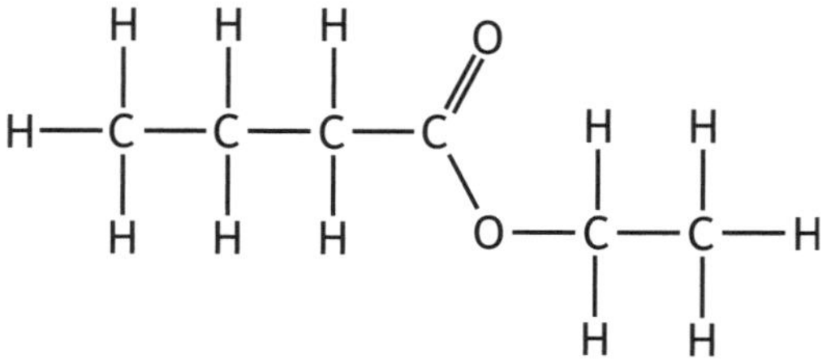

ethyl butanoate

MARKS

DO NOT WRITE IN THIS MARGIN

11. (continued)

Using your knowledge of chemistry, comment on how the differences in physical and chemical properties can be used to distinguish between the compounds extracted from orange juice.

3

[Turn over

DO NOT WRITE IN THIS MARGIN

12. The label from a bottle of pine fresh bleach cleaner is shown.

> **PINE FRESH BLEACH CLEANER**
>
> **Formulated to kill germs and remove stains**
>
> Ingredients:
> aqua, sodium hypochlorite, sodium hydroxide, less than 5% anionic surfactants, non-ionic surfactants, soap, perfume
>
> **WARNING!**
> Do not use together with other products. May release dangerous gases (chlorine)
>
> **DANGER**
> Keep out of reach of children
>
> **CORROSIVE**

(a) Surfactant molecules are added to bleach cleaner to act as detergents, soaps or emulsifiers.

Information on three of the surfactants in the bleach cleaner is shown in the table.

Surfactant structure	Type of surfactant	Head group
Compound A H_3C—CH_2—CH_2—CH_2—CH_2—CH_2—CH_2—CH_2—CH_2—CH_2—CH_2—CH_2—O—CH_2—CH_2—O—H	non-ionic	polar
Compound B $NH_3^+Cl^-$ attached to C with H_3C, CH, CH_3, CH_3 groups, and H_3C—CH_2—CH_2—CH_2—CH_2—CH_2—CH_2—CH_2—CH_2—CH_2—CH_2—CH_2—CH_2— chain		
Compound C $O{=}C{-}O^-Na^+$ attached to H_3C—CH_2—CH_2—CH_2—CH_2—CH_2—CH_2—CH_2—CH_2—CH_2—CH_2—CH_2—CH_2—CH_2—CH_2—CH_2—CH_2— chain	ionic	negatively charged

MARKS | DO NOT WRITE IN THIS MARGIN

12. **(a)** **(continued)**

(i) Complete the table for compound B. 1

(ii) Compound C is a soap molecule.

(A) Soaps can be made from fats and oils.

Name the reaction used to make soaps from fats and oils. 1

(B) Soap molecules allow oil to mix with water.

Compound C

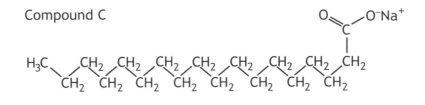

Explain fully the cleaning action of compound C. 3

You may wish to use diagrams to illustrate your answers.

[Turn over

MARKS | DO NOT WRITE IN THIS MARGIN

12. (a) (continued)

(iii) The structure of an emulsifier molecule is shown below.

State how emulsifiers are made from edible oils.

1

(b) Sodium hypochlorite, Na^+OCl^-, is the main active compound in bleach.

PINE FRESH BLEACH CLEANER

Formulated to kill germs and remove stains

Ingredients:
aqua, sodium hypochlorite, sodium hydroxide, less than 5% anionic surfactants, non-ionic surfactants, soap, perfume

WARNING!
Do not use together with other products. May release dangerous gases (chlorine)

DANGER
Keep out of reach of children

CORROSIVE

Sodium hypochlorite, Na^+OCl^-, is produced by reacting chlorine with sodium hydroxide solution.

$$Cl_2(g) + 2Na^+OH^-(aq) \rightarrow Na^+OCl^-(aq) + Na^+Cl^-(aq) + H_2O(\ell)$$

(i) A chlorine molecule has a pure covalent bond.

Explain what is meant by a pure covalent bond.

1

MARKS DO NOT WRITE IN THIS MARGIN

12. (b) (continued)

(ii) When the chlorine is reacted with sodium hydroxide solution an excess of sodium hydroxide is used.

Suggest why an excess of sodium hydroxide is used.   1

(c) In the bleach cleaner an equilibrium exists.

$$2H^+(aq) + OCl^-(aq) + Cl^-(aq) \quad Cl_2(g) + H_2O(\ell)$$

The label warns that the bleach cleaner should not be used with other products as it may release chlorine gas.

Explain clearly why mixing the bleach with an acid would shift the equilibrium to the right, resulting in the release of chlorine gas from the bleach cleaner.   2

[Turn over for next question

MARKS | DO NOT WRITE IN THIS MARGIN

12.   (continued)

(d) The concentration of hypochlorite, OCl^-, in bleach can be determined by a redox reaction that involves two steps.

Step 1

An excess of acidified potassium iodide is added to the bleach. This converts the iodide ions into iodine.

$$OCl^-(aq) + 2I^-(aq) + 2H^+(aq) \rightarrow I_2(aq) + Cl^-(aq) + H_2O(\ell)$$

Step 2

The iodine produced in step 1 is titrated with sodium thiosulfate, $Na_2S_2O_3$.

$$I_2(aq) + 2Na_2S_2O_3(aq) \rightarrow 2NaI(aq) + Na_2S_4O_6(aq)$$

(i) Write the ion-electron equation for the reduction reaction taking place in **Step 1**.   1

(ii) A $25\,cm^3$ sample of a diluted bleach was transferred into a conical flask and excess acidified potassium iodide added. The iodine produced was titrated with $0\cdot098\,mol\,l^{-1}$ $Na_2S_2O_3$, requiring an average volume of $9\cdot0\,cm^3$ to reach the end point.

Calculate the concentration, in $mol\,l^{-1}$, of sodium hypochlorite in the diluted bleach.   3

[END OF QUESTION PAPER]

MARKS | DO NOT WRITE IN THIS MARGIN

ADDITIONAL SPACE FOR ANSWERS AND ROUGH WORK

Additional diagram for question 1 (c)

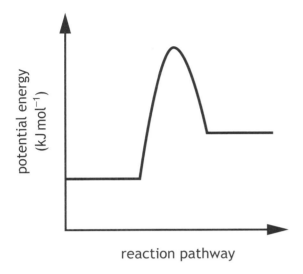

Additional diagram for question 9 (b)

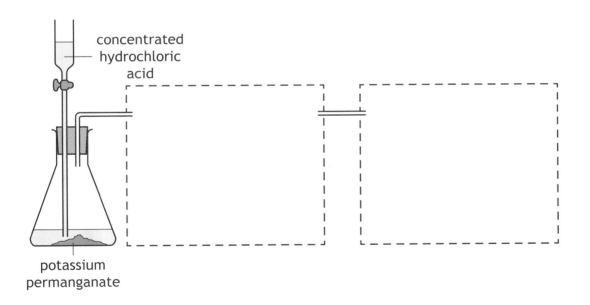

Additional diagram for question 10 (b) (ii)

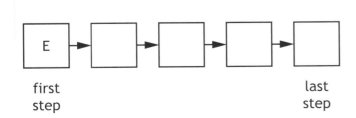

ADDITIONAL SPACE FOR ANSWERS AND ROUGH WORK

Page forty-two

MARKS | DO NOT WRITE IN THIS MARGIN

ADDITIONAL SPACE FOR ANSWERS AND ROUGH WORK

[BLANK PAGE]

DO NOT WRITE ON THIS PAGE

HIGHER CHEMISTRY
2018

Section 1

Question	Answer	Max Mark
1.	B	1
2.	A	1
3.	D	1
4.	C	1
5.	D	1
6.	C	1
7.	A	1
8.	D	1
9.	A	1
10.	B	1
11.	D	1
12.	D	1
13.	A	1
14.	A	1
15.	D	1
16.	C	1
17.	B	1
18.	C	1
19.	B	1
20.	B	1

Section 2

1. (a) (i) Electronegativity is the measure of attraction an atom/nucleus has for the electrons in a bond/shared electrons. **(1 mark)**

   (ii) (More shells) so increased shielding/more shielding.

   OR

   Covalent radius increases/atom size increases/more shells so attraction of the nucleus/protons for the (outer/shared) electrons decreases. **(1 mark)**

   (b) (Intermolecular) forces/bonds increase (going down the group). **(1)**

   LDFs are the forces (broken) between the molecules. **(1)**

   The more electrons the stronger the LDFs. **(1)**
   Maximum mark: 3

2. (a) Increasing number of protons (in the nucleus).

   OR

   Increasing/greater/stronger/higher nuclear charge (holds electrons more tightly). **(1 mark)**

(b) (i) Sulfur chloride should be circled. **(1 mark)**

   (ii) Silicon tetrachloride and hexane are non-polar. **(1)**

   Silicon tetrachloride is non-polar due to its shape/dipoles/polarities cancelling out. **(1)**
   Maximum mark: 2

(c) (i) Silicon nitride is a (covalent) network. **(1)**

   (Strong) covalent bonds are broken. **(1)**
   Maximum mark: 2

   (ii) $17 \cdot 934 / 17 \cdot 93 / 17 \cdot 9 / 18$ (%) **(2 marks)**

   Partial mark for correct use of atom economy relationship without correct use of stoichiometry (working must be shown).

   Partial marks

   Correct working with no correct answer given.

   $$\frac{140 \cdot 3}{(3 \times 170 \cdot 1) + (16 \times 17 \cdot 0)} \times 100$$

   $$\frac{140 \cdot 3}{510 \cdot 3 + 272 \cdot 0} \times 100$$

   $$\frac{140 \cdot 3}{782 \cdot 3} \times 100$$

   Incorrect use of stoichiometry.

   $$\frac{140 \cdot 3}{170 \cdot 1 + 17 \cdot 0} \times 100 = 74 \cdot 99$$

   $$\frac{140 \cdot 3}{3 \times 170 \cdot 1 + 17 \cdot 0} \times 100 = 26 \cdot 6$$

   $$\frac{140 \cdot 3}{170 \cdot 1 + 16 \times 17 \cdot 0} \times 100 = 31 \cdot 7$$

   Answer and working must be shown.

   $0 \cdot 179$ **(1 mark)**

(d) (i) Diagram shows a workable method for the passing of chlorine gas over heated aluminium.

   Aluminium must be labelled and there must be an indication of heat. Heated aluminium accepted. **(1)**

   Diagram allows aluminium chloride to be collected **in a flask** as a solid and chlorine gas to escape. **(1)**
   Maximum mark: 2

   (ii) To provide (initial) activation energy/(sufficient) energy to form activated (activation) complex. **(1 mark)**

3. (a) Heating mantle or hot plate
   OR
   (hot) water bath. **(1 mark)**

(b) Condense reactants or products/acts as a condenser/to prevent escape of (volatile/gaseous) reactants or products/to prevent the escape of gas(es). **(1 mark)**

(c) (i) Water (Accept formula H_2O) **(1 mark)**

(ii) Correctly calculates number of moles of:
Benzoic acid = 0·041
Methanol = 0·078.
OR
Working out that 1·31 g of methanol would be needed to react with 5 g of benzoic acid.
OR
Working out that 9·53 g of benzoic acid would be needed to react with 2·5 g of methanol. **(1)**
Statement demonstrating understanding of limiting reactant

e.g. there are less moles of benzoic acid therefore it is the limiting reactant.
OR
There are more moles of methanol therefore it is in excess.
OR
0·078 moles of methanol would require 0·078 moles of benzoic acid. **(1)**
Maximum mark: 2

(iii) (£)12·84 **(2)**
Partial Marks
Mass benzoic acid = 161·3(g).
OR
Cost to make 3·1g of methyl benzoate = (£) 0·398.
OR
Evidence of a calculated mass of benzoic acid × 7·96 or 8 (p). **(1)**
Maximum mark: 2

4. (a) Correctly drawn structure of pentan-2-one, pentan-3-one or 3-methylbutanone.
(Accept full or shortened structural formulae)
Maximum mark: 1

H   O
| ||
H_3C — C — C — CH_3
|
CH_3

O
||
H_3C — CH_2 — CH_2 — C — CH_3

O
||
H_3C — CH_2 — C — CH_2 — CH_3

(b) Fehling's solution/Tollens' reagent/**acidified** dichromate solution. **(1 mark)**

(c) Permanent dipole-permanent dipole (interactions/ attractions). **(1 mark)**

(d) Will react with oxygen/undergo oxidation. **(1)**
Forming a **carboxylic** acid (which has unpleasant taste). **(1)**
Maximum mark: 2

(e) (i) Because it has two molecules joining together with the loss of a small/water molecule. **(1 mark)**

(ii) 6-methylheptan-2-one **(1 mark)**

5. This is an open ended question

1 mark: The student has demonstrated, at an appropriate level, a limited understanding of the chemistry involved. The candidate has made some statement(s) which is/are relevant to the situation, showing that at least a little of the chemistry within the problem is understood.

2 marks: The student has demonstrated, at an appropriate level, a reasonable understanding of the chemistry involved. The student makes some statement(s) which is/are relevant to the situation, showing that the problem is understood.

3 marks: The maximum available mark would be awarded to a student who has demonstrated, at an appropriate level, a good understanding of the chemistry involved. The student shows a good comprehension of the chemistry of the situation and has provided a logically correct answer to the question posed. This type of response might include a statement of the principles involved, a relationship or an equation, and the application of these to respond to the problem. This does not mean the answer has to be what might be termed an 'excellent' answer or a 'complete' one.
Maximum mark: 3

6. (a) (i) (enzyme) hydrolysis **(1 mark)**

(ii) $C_{20}H_{29}OH$
OR
$C_{20}H_{30}O$ **(1 mark)**

(b) (i) Bond breaking by UV (light) or example of initiation reaction (equation or diagram).
e.g. chlorine splitting to give two free radicals is accepted, provided UV is shown. **(1 mark)**

(ii) propagation **(1 mark)**

(iii) Can react with free radicals forming stable molecules/free radicals (and prevent chain reactions).
OR
Donates electron(s).
OR
Acting as a reducing agent.
OR
Provide electrons to pair with an unpaired electron. **(1 mark)**

(c) (i) Circle any peptide link (CONH). **(1 mark)**

(ii) **(1 mark)**

OH
|
H CH_2 O
| | ||
H — N — C — C — OH
|
H

7. (a) (i)   (1 mark)

(ii) Sesquiterpene   (1 mark)

(b) (i) 5·345/5.35/5.3 (kg)   (2)

Partial marking

Mass of squalene

= 10·69 × 500 000

= 5 345 000 (mg)   (1)

OR

For incorrectly calculating mass in mg but correctly converting to kg.   (1)

OR

For incorrectly calculating mass of squalene but correctly multiplying this by 500 000.   (1)

OR

Conversion of 10·69 mg to kg

i.e. 10·69 × 10⁻⁶.   (1)

Maximum mark: 2

(ii) 6/six (moles)   (1 mark)

(c) (i) Addition

OR

hydration.   (1 mark)

(ii) (terpineol) is a tertiary alcohol (and cannot be oxidised).   (1 mark)

8. (a) 286 (kJ mol⁻¹)   (2)

Partial mark 1 mark

Evidence of the use of **all** the correct bond enthalpies (or correct multiples thereof) (412, 348, 838, 436 (ignore signs)).

OR

If only three values are retrieved, the candidate recognises that bond breaking is endothermic and bond formation is exothermic and correctly manipulates the bond enthalpy values they have used to give their answer.   Maximum mark: 2

(b) (+) 185 (kJ mol⁻¹)   (2 marks)

[(−1182) + (−572) + (+1939)]

= (+) 185 (kJ mol⁻¹)

Partial marks

Treat as two concepts. Either would be acceptable for 1 mark.

Evidence of understanding of reversal of third enthalpy value

i.e. +1939 or 1939 must be seen.

The other two enthalpy values (regardless of value) **must** be negative, or this partial mark cannot be awarded.

OR

Evidence of understanding of multiplying the first enthalpy value by 3 and the second enthalpy value by 2.

Ignore the enthalpy signs associated with these numbers

i.e. any combination of

3 (±394) **and** 2 (±286)

OR

±1182 **and** ±572

Multiplication of the third enthalpy value by any factor is taken as cancelling of this partial mark.

Maximum mark: 2

(c) (i) 48475 (kJ) (Also accepted: −48475 (kJ))   (1 mark)

(ii) 13·76/13·8/14 (g)   (2 marks)

Partial mark 1 mark

Mass of oxygen required = 3·2 (g)

OR

550·4 (g)   Maximum marks: 2

(iii) Methanol and ethanol contain oxygen in their structure, (so less additional oxygen is required).   (1 mark)

9. (a) (i) **1 mark each** for any two of the following points.

- recycle (waste) gases
- use catalyst
- low/reduce energy requirements
- reactors are run at low temperatures/the temperatures in the reactors is lowered
- inexpensive feedstocks
- selling/using by-products   (2 marks)

(ii) (fractional) distillation   (1 mark)

(b) Propan-1-ol has fewer hydroxyl groups than ethane-1,2-diol/ethane-1,2-diol has more hydroxyl groups/propan-1-ol has 1 hydroxyl group and ethane-1,2-diol has 2.   (1)

Weaker/fewer hydrogen bonds between propan-1-ol molecules.

OR

Stronger/more hydrogen bonds between ethane-1,2-diol molecules.   (1)

Maximum marks: 2

(c) Structure of propane-1,2-diol or propane-1,3-diol or propane-1,1-diol or propane-2,2-diol.   (1 mark)

OH
|
H₃C — C — CH₃
|
OH

$$H_3C - CH_2 - \overset{\overset{\displaystyle OH}{|}}{CH} - \overset{\overset{\displaystyle OH}{|}}{}$$

OH
|
H₃C — CH₂ — CH
|
OH

OH   OH
| |
H₃C — CH — CH₂

OH   OH
| |
H₂C — CH₂ — CH₂

(d) (i) Pipette (used to measure 20 cm³ of ethanol.) **(1)**

Statement of use of **volumetric/standard** flask to make up to/fill to the mark/to 100 cm³. **(1)**

Maximum marks: 2

(ii) 157·5(cm³) **(1 mark)**

(iii) (A) **(1 mark)**

OR

OR

OR

OR

(iii) (B) Correct molecular formula (NaC₂H₃O₃)
OR
shortened structural formula (HOCH₂COONa)
OR
any full structural formula which shows the correct salt. **(1 mark)**

10. This is an open ended question

1 mark: The student has demonstrated, at an appropriate level, a limited understanding of the chemistry involved. The candidate has made some statement(s) which is/are relevant to the situation, showing that at least a little of the chemistry within the problem is understood.

2 marks: The student has demonstrated, at an appropriate level, a reasonable understanding of the chemistry involved. The student makes some statement(s) which is/are relevant to the situation, showing that the problem is understood.

3 marks: The maximum available mark would be awarded to a student who has demonstrated, at an appropriate level, a good understanding of the chemistry involved. The student shows a good comprehension of the chemistry of the situation and has provided a logically correct answer to the question posed. This type of response might include a statement of the principles involved, a relationship or an equation, and the application of these to respond to the problem. This does not mean the answer has to be what might be termed an 'excellent' answer or a 'complete' one. **Maximum mark: 3**

11. (a) Correct description of weighing by difference.
OR
Correct description of use of the Tare function. **(1 mark)**

(b) $2I^- (aq) \rightarrow I_2(aq) + 2e^-$
OR
$2I^- (aq) \rightarrow I_2(s) + 2e^-$ **(1 mark)**

(c) (i) 9·5(cm³) **(1 mark)**

(ii) $4·75 \times 10^{-6}$ moles **(2 marks)**
Partial mark for correct use of mole ratio.
OR
Determination of number of moles without using the mole ratio. **Maximum marks: 2**

12. (a) (i) More/adding chlorine(s). **(1)**
More/adding carbon(s).
OR
Adding an alkyl/hydrocarbon chain/group.
OR
Longer/bigger carbon/hydrocarbon/alkyl (chain/group). **(1)**
(2 marks)

(ii) 2-chloro-4,5-dimethylphenol **(1 mark)**

(b) (i) 126·9/127(kg)
Partial mark either for:
Calculation of the theoretical yield 141 (no unit required) **(1)**
OR
for correctly calculating 90% of an incorrectly calculated theoretical yield. **(1)**
(2 marks)

(ii) Propanone
OR
Acetone
OR
Propan-2-one. **(1 mark)**

HIGHER CHEMISTRY
2018 SPECIMEN QUESTION PAPER

Section 1

Question	Answer	Max Mark
1.	A	1
2.	D	1
3.	B	1
4.	C	1
5.	B	1
6.	C	1
7.	D	1
8.	D	1
9.	A	1
10.	B	1
11.	B	1
12.	C	1
13.	B	1
14.	A	1
15.	C	1
16.	A	1
17.	C	1
18.	C	1
19.	B	1
20.	D	1
21.	A	1
22.	A	1
23.	A	1
24.	D	1
25.	B	1

Section 2

1. (a) (i) Boron
   OR
   Carbon
   OR
   B
   OR
   C **(1 mark)**

   (ii) Increasing/greater/stronger/higher nuclear charge
   OR
   Increasing/greater/higher number of protons
   (1 mark)

   (iii) Lithium
   OR
   Li **(1 mark)**

(b) Electrons are further from the nucleus
   OR
   Atomic size increases
   OR
   Extra energy level **(1)**
   Increased screening/shielding **(1)**
   Maximum marks: 2

(c) Covalent molecular **(1 mark)**

2. (a) Award up to 3 marks for answers containing the following points:
   Br_2 non-polar/I-Cl polar
   OR
   ICl has permanent dipole- permanent dipole interactions **(1)**
   Br_2 and ICl have same number of electrons
   OR
   Strength of LDF Br_2 and ICl similar **(1)**
   Boiling point of ICl higher than boiling point of Br_2
   OR
   Intermolecular forces are broken when a substance boils **(1)**
   Maximum marks: 3

(b) H_2/hydrogen **(1 mark)**

(c) (i) Cl—H + H· **(1)**
   H—H / H_2 **(1)**
   Maximum marks: 2

   (ii) To prevent light/UV shining on sample
   OR
   To prevent initiation
   OR
   To prevent radicals from forming
   OR
   To prevent (glass/tube) shattering **(1 mark)**

   (iii) -185 (kJ mol^{-1}) **(2 marks)**
   Partial marking:
   A single mark is available if either of the following operations is correctly executed.
   EITHER
   The three relevant bond enthalpy values are retrieved; 436, 243 and 432
   OR
   Correct use of incorrect bond enthalpy values

(d) $10Cl^-(aq) + 2MnO_4^-(aq) + 16H^+(aq)$
   $\downarrow$
   $5Cl_2(g) + 2Mn^{2+}(aq) + 8H_2O(\ell)$ **(1 mark)**

3. (a) (i) (A) Butyl propanoate **(1 mark)**
   (B) B>A>C **(1 mark)**
   (ii) (A) Carbonyl **(1 mark)**

   (B)
   (1 mark)

(b) Any one of the four following groups of atoms circled

(1 mark)

(c) (i) Award up to 3 marks for the following points:
Sodium lauryl sulfate has both hydrophobic/
oil-soluble and hydrophilic/water-soluble parts

OR

Sodium lauryl sulfate has both ionic and
non-polar parts (1)

Correct identification of the parts of this
molecule which dissolve in water and oil (1)

Formation (by agitation) of a 'balllike'
structure/globule (with the oil/grease held
inside the ball) or micelle or mention of an
emulsion (1)

Repulsion of micelles (due to negatively charged
heads) (1)
Maximum marks: 3

(ii) Do not form scum/precipitates (with hard
water) **(1 mark)**

(d) **Award 1 mark** where the candidate has
demonstrated, at an appropriate level, a limited
understanding of the chemistry involved. They have
made some statement(s) which are relevant to the
situation, showing that they have understood at
least a little of the chemistry within the problem.

Award 2 marks where the candidate has
demonstrated, at an appropriate level, a reasonable
understanding of the chemistry involved. They
make some statement(s) which are relevant to the
situation, showing that they have understood the
problem.

Award 3 marks where the candidate has
demonstrated, at an appropriate level, a good
understanding of the chemistry involved. They
show a good comprehension of the chemistry of the
situation and provide a logically correct answer to
the question posed. This type of response might
include a statement of the principles involved, a
relationship or an equation, and the application of
these to respond to the problem. The answer does
not need to be 'excellent' or 'complete' for the
candidate to gain full marks.

Award 0 marks where the candidate has not
demonstrated, at an appropriate level, an
understanding of the chemistry involved. There is
no evidence that they have recognised the area
of chemistry involved, or they have not given any
statement of a relevant chemistry principle. Award
this mark also if the candidate merely restates the
chemistry given in the question. **Maximum marks: 3**

4. (a) (i) Shea butter has fewer double bonds/is not very
unsaturated (1)

Unsaturated molecules cannot pack tightly

OR

Saturated molecules can pack tightly (1)

The London dispersion forces/van der Waals'
forces between its molecules are stronger (than
in oils) (1)
Maximum marks: 3

(ii) 139 − 149 **(1 mark)**

(b) (i) Glycerol/propane-1,2,3-triol **(1 mark)**

(ii) 24·8 or 25 (%) **(3 marks)**

Partial marking:
Calculation of theoretical yield of soap omitting
mole ratio (1·72 (g))

OR

Correctly calculated number of moles of reactant **and** product; 0·00566 and 0·00421 **(1)**

Use of correct mole ratio 1:3 **(1)**

Correctly calculated % yield using the actual mass and an incorrectly calculated theoretical mass

OR

Correctly calculated % yield using incorrectly calculated numbers of moles of product and reactant **(1)**

5. (a) −43·9 (kJ mol⁻¹) **(2 marks)**

Partial marking:

Evidence of understanding of reversal of first **and** final equations, with second equation unchanged **(1)**

(b) (i) (£) 1045 **(2 marks)**

Partial marking:

A single mark is available if any one of the following operations is correctly executed.

Calculating the cost of the reactants required to prepare 5·75 g of butan2ol: £60·11

OR

Calculating the mass of both reactants needed to produce 100 g of butan-2-ol: 87·1 g of propanal and 347·8 g of CH_3MgBr

OR

Having incorrectly calculated the cost of the reactants required to prepare 5·75 g of butan-2-ol, correctly scaling their calculated cost by 100/5·75 to obtain the cost to produce 100 g of butan-2-ol

(ii) Hexan-2-ol **(1 mark)**
(Accept 2-hexanol)

(c) (i) Oxidation **(1 mark)**

(ii) −3 (°C) **(1 mark)**

6. (a) Shape maintained by intermolecular bonds (between side chains on protein) **(1)**

These bonds broken when the protein is heated **(1)**
Maximum marks: 2

(b) (i) Gentle method of heating

OR

Can control temperature easily

OR

To prevent the protein structure changing/ denaturing

OR

Mention of flammability **(1 mark)**

(ii) Sodium oxide

OR

Sodium hydroxide

OR

Sodium carbonate

OR

Sodium hydrogen carbonate **(1 mark)**

(iii) **(1 mark)**

OR

OR

(c) 4 or 4·0 (mg) **(1 mark)**

(d) Eight or 8 **(1 mark)**

7. (a) Carboxyl (group)

OR

Carboxylic acid (group)

(b) (i) 100 (%) **(1 mark)**

(ii) Curve starting at the level representing the reactants and finishing at the level representing the products but with a maximum, or maxima, below the existing maximum **(1 mark)**

(c) (i) Large hydrocarbon section/non-polar chain (attached to the carboxyl group) **(1 mark)**

(ii) (A) (It is an) emulsifier

OR

To stop layers forming **(1 mark)**

(B) 2·5 (cm³) **(1 mark)**

8. (a) Any correctly drawn diagram showing an oxygen atom attracted to a hydrogen atom within a hydroxyl group/water e.g.

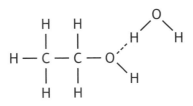

OR

(1 mark)

(b)

$$CH_3 - \overset{\overset{\displaystyle CH_3}{|}}{CH} - CH_2 - OH$$

(1 mark)

(c) 12 200 cm³ or 12·2 litres

Partial marking:

Where the correct value for the volume has not been calculated, one mark is available for either:

The correct strategy to calculate the mass of 2-methylpropan-1-ol required: $\frac{351000}{36\cdot1}$ or 9720

OR

The correct strategy to work out the volume of 2-methylpropan-1-ol required: *mass in g* × 1·25 or $\frac{351000}{28\cdot88}$

OR

A correct strategy to work out the energy released per cm³: $\frac{36\cdot1}{1\cdot25}$ or 28·88

One mark is also available where the candidate gives the correct unit for volume in their final answer.

9. (a) (i) A solution of exactly/accurately/precisely known concentration **(1 mark)**

(ii) 221 (mg) **(2 marks)**

Partial marking:

A single mark is available if any one of the following operations is correctly executed.
The GFM of NaF has been calculated correctly: 42 (g)

OR

The number of moles of fluoride ions has been calculated correctly: 0·00526

(iii) Dissolve (sample) in a small/minimum volume of (deionised) water **(1)**

Transfer with rinsings **(1)**

Make up to the mark in a volumetric/standard flask **(1)**

Maximum marks: 3

(iv) (Tap water) might contain fluoride ions.

OR

(Tap water) might contain species that interfere with the reaction.

OR

(Tap water) might be coloured. **(1 mark)**

(v) 1·5 − 2·0 (mg l⁻¹) **(1 mark)**

(b) (i) Pipette **(1 mark)**

(ii) 0·0324 (mol l⁻¹) **(3 marks)**

Partial marking:

Two 'concept' marks are available.

For correct use of the relationship between concentration, number of moles and volume:

e.g. by calculating a number of moles by multiplying a concentration by a volume and/or by calculating a concentration by dividing a number of moles by a volume, and/or calculating a number of moles

OR

For inserting correct pairings for *c* and *v* concentrations and volumes into the formula $\frac{c_1v_1}{n_1} = \frac{c_2v_2}{n_2}$ **(1)**

For appreciation that this reaction demonstrates a 2:5 stoichiometry: eg by multiplying a number of moles by either $\frac{2}{5}$ or $\frac{5}{2}$

OR

For substitution of the numbers 2 and 5 into as values for *n* in the formula $\frac{c_1v_1}{n_1} = \frac{c_2v_2}{n_2}$ **(1)**

10. (a) (i) When a molecule reacts with water to break down/apart (into smaller molecules) **(1 mark)**

(ii) Methanol **(1 mark)**

(iii) Essential (amino acids) **(1 mark)**

(b) (i) 69 − 70 (mg) **(1 mark)**

(ii) Sample of **Y** should be diluted **(1 mark)**

OR

Less of sample **Y** should be used

OR

Smaller sample of **Y**

11. (a) 2NaOH + Cl₂ → NaClO + NaCl + H₂O **(1 mark)**

(b) ClO⁻ + 2H⁺ + 2e⁻ → Cl⁻ + H₂O **(1 mark)**

(c) (i) Gas-tight reaction vessel fitted with delivery tube **(1)**

Method for collecting and measuring the volume of gas produced **(1)**

Hydrogen peroxide, bleach and oxygen labelled in correct position **(1)**

Maximum marks: 3

(ii) 0·67 (mol l⁻¹) **(3 marks)**

Partial marking:

Correct use of the relationship between volume of gas and number of moles, e.g. a volume of oxygen, in whatever unit, being divided by the molar volume, in whatever unit **(1)**

Correct use of the relationship between the concentration of a solution, the number of moles of solute and the volume of solution, e.g. a value that the candidate believes to be the number of moles of ClO⁻ divided by the volume of the solution, in whatever unit. **(1)**

12. (a) (i) Purple to colourless **(1 mark)**

(ii) 83 or 83·3 (s) **(2 marks)**

Partial marking:
A single mark is available if either of the following operations is correctly executed:
Reading rate correctly from graph: 0·012 (s^{-1})
OR
Correctly calculating the reaction time from an incorrect value for the relative rate.

(b) (i) The peak of the curve should be to the left and higher than the original peak. **(1 mark)**

(ii) A vertical line should have been drawn at a lower kinetic energy than the original Ea shown on graph. **(1 mark)**

(c) Incorrect orientation/geometry **(1 mark)**
OR
Activated complex breaks up to reform the reactants

13. Award 1 mark where the candidate has demonstrated, at an appropriate level, a limited understanding of the chemistry involved. They have made some statement(s) which are relevant to the situation, showing that they have understood at least a little of the chemistry within the problem.

Award 2 marks where the candidate has demonstrated, at an appropriate level, a reasonable understanding of the chemistry involved. They make some statement(s) which are relevant to the situation, showing that they have understood the problem.

Award 3 marks where the candidate has demonstrated, at an appropriate level, a good understanding of the chemistry involved. They show a good comprehension of the chemistry of the situation and provide a logically correct answer to the question posed. This type of response might include a statement of the principles involved, a relationship or an equation, and the application of these to respond to the problem. The answer does not need to be 'excellent' or 'complete' for the candidate to gain full marks.

Award 0 marks where the candidate has not demonstrated, at an appropriate level, an understanding of the chemistry involved. There is no evidence that they have recognised the area of chemistry involved, or they have not given any statement of a relevant chemistry principle. Award this mark also if the candidate merely restates the chemistry given in the question. **Maximum mark: 3**

HIGHER CHEMISTRY 2019

Section 1

Question	Answer	Max Mark
1.	C	1
2.	B	1
3.	A	1
4.	C	1
5.	B	1
6.	A	1
7.	D	1
8.	B	1
9.	D	1
10.	D	1
11.	C	1
12.	B	1
13.	D	1
14.	A	1
15.	C	1
16.	D	1
17.	B	1
18.	B	1
19.	B	1
20.	C	1
21.	A	1
22.	D	1
23.	C	1
24.	A	1
25.	D	1

Section 2

1. (a) (i) $Na_2S_2O_3 + 2HCl \rightarrow S + SO_2 + 2NaCl + H_2O$
Correct multiples accepted. **(1 mark)**

(ii) (A)

Experiment	Volume of water (cm^3)
A	0
B	10
C	20
D	30
E	40

All entries correct **(1 mark)**

(B) 35/35·1/35·09 (seconds or s) **(1 mark)**

(iii) 12 +/− 1 (°C) **(1 mark)**

(b) (Particles must have) sufficient or enough energy (to react).
OR
(Particles must have) energy equal to or greater than the activation energy or E_A.

OR

(Particles must have) minimum/enough energy to form an activated complex. **(1)**

(Collision must occur with) suitable/correct/geometry/orientation. **(1)**

Maximum marks: 2

(c) (i) X shown at peak of curve. **(1 mark)**

(ii)

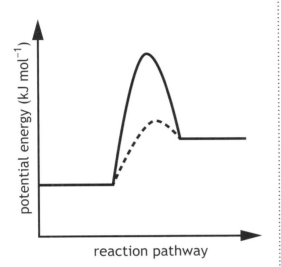

reaction pathway

(1 mark)

2. (a) (i) Increasing/greater/stronger/larger nuclear charge (holds electrons more tightly).

OR

Increasing number of protons. **(1 mark)**

(ii) (More shells) so increased/more screening/shielding.

OR

Covalent radius increases/atom size increases/more shells so attraction of the nucleus/protons for the **outer electron** decreases. **(1 mark)**

(b) (i) $N^+(g) \rightarrow N^{2+}(g) + e^-$ **(1 mark)**

(ii) The 6th ionisation energy involves removing an electron from the shell which is inner/full (whole)/(more) stable/closer to the nucleus

OR

the 6th electron is removed from the electron shell which is inner/full (whole)/(more) stable/closer to the nucleus. **(1 mark)**

The 6th electron is less shielded.

OR

the 6th electron is more strongly attracted to/pulled towards the nucleus. **(1 mark)**

(c) Al forms Al^{3+}/loses electrons to form an ion **and** P forms P^{3-}/gains electrons to form an ion. **(1 mark)**

Aluminium ion has one less energy level than phosphide/phosphorus ion.

OR

Phosphide/phosphorus ion has one more energy level than aluminium ion. **(1 mark)**

(d) (Radius ratio =) 0·96, (hence) caesium chloride (or correct formula). **(1 mark)**

3. This is an open ended question

1 mark: The student has demonstrated, at an appropriate level, a limited understanding of the chemistry involved. The student has made some statement(s) which is/are relevant to the situation, showing that at least a little of the chemistry within the problem is understood.

2 marks: The student has demonstrated a reasonable understanding, at an appropriate level, of the chemistry involved. The student makes some statement(s) which is/are relevant to the situation, showing that the problem is understood.

3 marks: The maximum available mark would be awarded to a student who has demonstrated a good understanding, at an appropriate level, of the chemistry involved. The student shows a good comprehension of the chemistry of the situation and has provided a logically correct answer to the question posed. This type of response might include a statement of the principles involved, a relationship or an equation, and the application of these to respond to the problem. This does not mean the answer has to be what might be termed an 'excellent' answer or a 'complete' one.

4. (a) (i) biological catalyst **(1 mark)**

(ii) 4·5/4·49/4·485 (%) **(1 mark)**

(b) (i) Carbon dioxide/CO_2 **(1 mark)**

(ii) (A) 0·25/0·3 **(1 mark)**

(B) (Cider) B or (sample) 4 **(1 mark)**

(c) propan-1,2,3-triol **(1 mark)**

OR

propane-1,2,3-triol

OR

1,2,3-propanetriol

(d) (i) (procyanidin B2) molecule is polar due to its **hydroxyl** groups

(−)**OH** accepted as hydroxyl

OR

(procyanidin B2) can form hydrogen bonds due to its **hydroxyl** groups **(1 mark)**

an explanation which links solubility of the molecule (procyanidin B2) to the polarity of water/hydrogen bonding of water. **(1 mark)**

(ii) 2-methylbutanoic acid **(1 mark)**

(iii) Isoprene(s) **(1 mark)**

OR

2-methylbuta-1,3-diene.

(e) (i) carbonyl **(1 mark)**

(ii) ethanoic acid/CH_3COOH **(1 mark)**

5. (a) (i) −694 (kJ mol⁻¹) **(2 marks)**

Bond breaking

$(4 \times 412) + (2 \times 498) = 2644$

Bond forming

$[(2 \times 743) + (4 \times 463)] = -3338$

A single mark is available if either of the following operations is correctly executed.

Either

The four relevant values for bond enthalpies of the C—H, O=O, C=O, and O—H (or multiples thereof) are retrieved from the data booklet (412, 498, 743, 463 – ignore signs).

OR

If only three correct values are retrieved, the candidate recognises that bond breaking is endothermic and bond forming is exothermic and have correctly manipulated the bond enthalpies and multiples that they have used with working shown.

(ii) Mean bond enthalpy must refer to an average energy and to a number of compounds and bond enthalpy must relate to one compound/diatomic molecule. **(1 mark)**

(iii) 0·367/0·37/0·4 (g) **(2 marks)**

Partial marking:

$n = V/V_m = 0.2/24 = 0.008333$ **(1)**

An incorrectly calculated number of moles **based on gas volume** $\times$ 44 **(1)**

24 l → 44 g **(1)**

Follow through from incorrect multiples of 24 l **or** 44 g **(1)**
(Maximum marks: 2)

(b) (i) (Record the) mass/weight of the burner before and after (heating the water) **(1 mark)**

(ii) –3496 (kJ mol^{-1}) **(3 marks)**

If final answer is wrong a maximum of 2 marks for the following concepts may be awarded

1 mark for a demonstration of the correct use of the relationship

$E_h = cm\Delta T$ as shown by

$(4.18 \times$ (an order of magnitude of 4) $\times 23)$

(ignore units for this mark).

1 mark for evidence of the knowledge that enthalpy of combustion relates to 1 mole, evidenced by the scaling up of a calculated value of energy released.

(iii) **1 mark** for any of the following **(1 mark)**

• Loss of heat/energy to the surroundings

• Incomplete combustion (of heptane/alkane)

• Loss (of heptane/alkane) by evaporation

• No lid on container

• No stirring

• Absorption of heat by glass/beaker or copper can.

6. (a) (i) (A) Same number of electrons (34). **(1 mark)**

OR

same strength of London dispersion forces/LDFs. **(1 mark)**

(B) Propan-1-ol has stronger intermolecular/ Van der Waal's forces than ethanethiol or vice versa.

OR

The intermolecular forces in propan-1-ol take more energy to break than those in ethanethiol or vice versa. **(1 mark)**

1 mark for identifying that the intermolecular forces in propan-1-ol are hydrogen bonds AND those in ethanethiol are permanent dipole – permanent dipole interactions/ attractions. **(1 mark)**

(ii) methanethiol **(1 mark)**

(iii) 11·853/11·85/11·9/12 mg – units required **(2 marks)**

Correctly calculated mass of ethanethiol without units. **(1 mark)**

Appropriate units **(1 mark)**

Mass (1)	Units (1)
12	mg
0·012	g
1.2×10^{-5}	kg

(b) (i) SH group is on a carbon connected to 3 other carbons/SH group is opposite the branch in a chain.

The SH group is attached to a carbon which has no hydrogens attached. **(1 mark)**

(ii) (A) **(1 mark)**

(B) 41·2 (g) **(2)**

OR

correct calculation of

Theoretical mass = 49·07 (g) **(1)**

Allow follow on from incorrect calculation of theoretical mass for **1 mark**

7. (a) (i) propagation **(1 mark)**

(ii) UV/ultraviolet **(1 mark)**

(iii) Anti-oxidant/free radical scavenger/reducing agent/electron donor. **(1 mark)**

(b) (i) Water/H_2O **(1 mark)**

(ii) **(1 mark)**

(iii) 3-hydroxybutanoic acid **(1 mark)**

8. (a) (i) 6 **(1 mark)**

(ii) London dispersion forces
Accept LDF. **(1 mark)**

(b) (i) dissolve the gelatin (in a small volume of water). **(1 mark)**

transfer quantitatively/with rinsings/washings. **(1 mark)**

fill to the mark/line (of the volumetric flask). **(1 mark)**

(ii) 11·0/11 **(1 mark)**

(c) (i) Bromelain/enzyme changes shape or denatured. **(1 mark)**

Bromelain/enzyme hydrogen bonds broken.

(ii) 38/37·9/37·88 (g) **(1 mark)**

9. (a) (i) (+) 220 (+/− 2) (kJ mol^{-1}) **(1 mark)**

(ii) (Increasing temperature) favours the endothermic/reverse reaction.

OR

The (forward) reaction is exothermic.

OR

The reverse reaction is endothermic. **(1 mark)**

(b) Diagram shows a workable method for removal of HCl(g) allowing transfer of chlorine gas.

Water/H_2O must be labelled. **(1 mark)**

Diagram shows a workable method of collecting a gas (e.g. a gas syringe). **(1 mark)**

(c) −391 (kJ mol^{-1}) **(2 marks)**

Partial marks

Treat as two concepts. Either would be acceptable for **1 mark**.

Evidence of understanding of reversal of first enthalpy value.

ie +75 must be seen.

The other two enthalpy values (regardless of value) **must** be negative, or this partial mark cannot be awarded.

OR

Evidence of understanding of multiplying the third enthalpy value by 4(±92).

OR

±368

Multiplication of any other enthalpy value by any factor is taken as cancelling of this partial mark.

10. (a) Chloride ions/magnesium ions/metal ions/salts may be present in tap water or not present/less in deionised/distilled water. **(1 mark)**

(b) (i)

Measurement	Apparatus
20·0 cm^3 (accurately)	Pipette
35 cm^3 (approximately)	Measuring cylinder

1 mark for each correct entry

(ii)

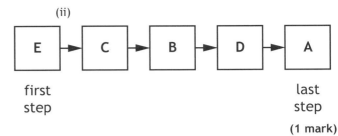

first step
last step

(1 mark)

All correct for **1 mark**.

(iii) 0·463/0·46/0·5 (g) **(2 marks)**

Partial marking **(1 mark)**

1 mark for knowledge of relationship between moles of silver chloride and magnesium chloride. This could be shown by a calculated number of moles of silver chloride correctly divided by 2.

OR

Incorrect mole ratio used but the relationship between moles and mass used correctly twice.

OR

by proportion

95·3 ↔ 286·8 (2 x 143·4).

OR

Mole ratio not applied correctly but proportion used correctly.

(c) 96/96·0 (%) **(1 mark)**

11. This is an open ended question

1 mark: The student has demonstrated, at an appropriate level, a limited understanding of the chemistry involved. The student has made some statement(s) which is/are relevant to the situation, showing that at least a little of the chemistry within the problem is understood.

2 marks: The student has demonstrated a reasonable understanding, at an appropriate level, of the chemistry involved. The student makes some statement(s) which is/are relevant to the situation, showing that the problem is understood.

3 marks: The maximum available mark would be awarded to a student who has demonstrated a good understanding, at an appropriate level, of the chemistry involved. The student shows a good comprehension of the chemistry of the situation and has provided a logically correct answer to the question posed. This type of response might include a statement of the principles involved, a relationship or an equation, and the application of these to respond to the problem. This does not mean the answer has to be what might be termed an 'excellent' answer or a 'complete' one.

(Maximum marks: 3)

12. (a) (i) Ionic and positively charged **(1 mark)**

Both needed

(ii) (A) alkaline hydrolysis/saponification. **(1 mark)**

(B) (Compound C) has an ionic/hydrophilic part **and** a non polar/hydrophobic part (or alternative wording/diagram showing knowledge of these parts of the molecule). **(1)**

Correctly identifies the part of the molecule/ head/COO⁻ dissolves in water/ is hydrophilic and the part of the molecule/tail/hydrocarbon chain dissolves in oil/is hydrophobic. **(1)**

Agitation separates oil from the surface/cause small oil droplets to form.

OR

The (negatively-charged) ball-like structures repel each other (and the oil or grease is kept suspended in the water).

OR

Soaps/compound C allow(s) emulsions to form or break(s) oil into micelles. **(1)**

Accept correct diagrams with annotations that show above. **Maximum marks: 3**

(iii) Reacting them (edible oils) with glycerol/ propan-1,2,3-triol/propane-1,2,3-triol/1,2,3-propanetriol **(1 mark)**

(b) (i) Both nuclei have the same attraction for the bonding electrons.

OR

Both atoms have same electronegativity/or electronegativity values given.

OR

Bonding electrons shared evenly. **(1 mark)**

(ii) **1 mark** for any of the following

- To ensure all chlorine is used up/to prevent chlorine being released
- NaOH is the cheaper/less expensive reactant
- To ensure that the bleach cleaner contains sodium hydroxide
- Excess NaOH would neutralise any acid added to cleaner
- Excess NaOH helps break up oil/grease.

(1 mark)

(c) (Adding acid) adds/increases H^+ (ions)

Rate of forward reaction is increased/speeds up (by addition of acid). **(2 marks)**

(d) (i) $OCl^-_{(aq)} + 2H^+_{(aq)} + 2e^- \rightarrow Cl^-_{(aq)} + H_2O_{(l)}$

(1 mark)

(ii) 1.76×10^{-2} (mol l⁻¹) **(3 marks)**

Partial marks can be awarded using a scheme of two 'concept' marks, and one 'arithmetic' mark.

1 mark for knowledge of the relationship between moles, concentration and volume.

This could be shown by one of the following steps:

Calculation of moles thiosulfate solution e.g. $0.098 \times 0.009 = 0.000882$

OR

calculation of concentration of iodine solution e.g. $0.000441/0.025$

OR

Insertion of correct pairings of values for concentration and volume in a valid titration formula.

1 mark for knowledge of relationship between moles of thiosulfate and hypochlorite. This could be shown by one of the following steps:

Calculation of moles hypochlorite from moles thiosulfate e.g. $0.000882/2 = 0.000441$.

OR

Insertion of correct stoichiometric values in a valid titration formula.

1 mark is awarded for correct arithmetic through the calculation. This mark can only be awarded if both concept marks have been awarded.